Upper limb disorders in the workplace

workplace

HSG60(rev)

© *Crown copyright 2002*

Applications for reproduction should be made in writing to:
Copyright Unit, Her Majesty's Stationery Office,
St Clements House, 2-16 Colegate, Norwich NR3 1BQ

First published 1990
Reprinted 1994, 1997, 1998, 2000
Second edition 2002

ISBN 0 7176 1978 8

This guidance is issued by the Health and Safety
Executive. Following the guidance is not compulsory and
you are free to take other action. But if you do follow the
guidance you will normally be doing enough to comply
with the law. Health and safety inspectors seek to secure
compliance with the law and may refer to this guidance
as illustrating good practice.

The Health and Safety Executive gratefully acknowledges
the assistance of *Boots Contract Manufacturing, BBC,*
Cadbury Ltd and *Ladbrokes* in compiling the case studies in
Appendix 1.

HSE would also like to thank the many individuals,
companies and organisations who have contributed to
the publication.

Contents

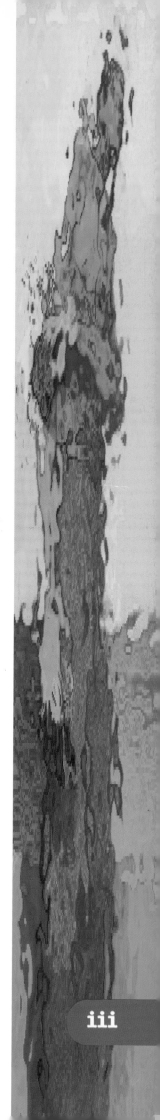

iii

Preface

The Health and Safety Commission (HSC) has a strategy for tackling musculoskeletal disorders (MSDs)* including upper limb disorders. The strategy adopts the principles of Securing Health *Together: A long-term occupational health strategy for England, Scotland and Wales.*[1] This forms an integral part of *Revitalising Health and Safety.*[2]

Government departments in co-operation with employers, employees, trade unions, employer's organisations, health professionals and voluntary groups have set several challenging targets as part of *Securing Health Together*. These have been used in establishing an HSC priority programme for musculoskeletal disorders with the following targets, to be achieved by 2010:

- 20% reduction in incidence of work-related ill health caused by MSDs;
- 30% reduction in the number of working days lost due to MSDs.

The priority programme aims to improve compliance with the law, to promote continuous improvement, and to develop the necessary knowledge, skills and support systems to achieve the MSD targets. This guidance forms one strand of the support to be provided for employers, employees and those who advise them. It aims to ensure that they have the right information and advice to prevent and manage upper limb disorders in the workplace.

---

* The term musculoskeletal disorders (MSDs) refers to problems affecting the muscles, tendons, ligaments, nerves or other soft tissues and joints. Upper limb disorders are a subcategory of MSDs.

Introduction

Understand the issues and commit to action	■ Is the risk of ULDs recognised in your workplace? ■ Is management committed to preventing or minimising the risk of ULDs? ■ Are there adequate management systems and policies to support this commitment?
Create the right organisational environment	■ Is worker participation actively sought and valued? ■ Are safety representatives involved? ■ Are all departments aware of the contribution they can make? ■ Is competence ensured? ■ Have you allocated responsibilities?
Assess the risk of ULDs in your workplace	■ Are any ULDs hazards identified through simple checks? ■ Are risk factors for ULDs present? Repetition Working environment Working posture Psychosocial factors Force Individual differences Duration of exposure
Reduce the risk of ULDs	■ Have you prioritised your actions to control the risks of ULDs? ■ Have you looked for 'higher order' solutions? ■ Have you utilized an ergonomics approach? ■ Have you implemented solutions?
Educate and inform your workforce	■ Have you educated and informed your workforce to help prevention? ■ Have you involved safety representatives in communicating information about ULDs risk factors and control measures? ■ What steps have you taken to ensure that training reinforces safe work practices and control measures?
Manage any episodes of ULDs	■ Have you implemented and supported a system for early reporting of systems for ULDs? ■ Do you actively look for symptoms of ULDs? ■ Have you arranged for occupational health provision? ■ Do you have systems in place for employees returning to work after an ULD?
Carry out regular checks on programme effectiveness	■ Do you have systems in place to monitor and review your controls for ULDs? ■ Do you have systems in place to monitor and review your ULDs management programme? ■ Are you aware of new developments/information? ■ Do you aim for continuous improvement?

Figure 1   **Framework for the management of ULD risks**

1   This document describes how managers, together with their employees, can cooperate to minimise the risks of upper limb disorders (ULDs) through a positive management approach. It gives general guidance on the processes involved and includes a risk assessment filter and worksheets as well as information on the medical aspects of ULDs and the legal requirements.

2   ULDs are conditions which affect the muscles, tendons, ligaments, nerves or other soft tissues and joints. The upper limb includes the neck, shoulders, arms, wrists, hands and fingers. ULDs can occur in almost any workplace and they can usually be prevented. When prevention has not worked, systems are needed to make sure they are promptly reported, properly diagnosed and treated. Employers' legal responsibility to prevent work-related accidents and ill health also applies to ULDs.

3   This guidance replaces *Work-related upper limb disorders: A guide to prevention* and reflects the changes in our understanding of risk factors and control strategies which have emerged from research over the last decade. This has shown the importance of psychosocial risk factors acting in conjunction with physical risk factors. It has demonstrated the need for an integrated approach to the management of ULD risks which addresses both organisational and physical aspects of the individual's task and work environment.

4   This guidance presents an approach which is based on seven stages in a management cycle. The stages are:

   ■   understand the issues and commit to action;
   ■   create the right organisational environment;
   ■   assess the risk of ULDs in your workplace;
   ■   reduce the risks of ULDs;
   ■   educate and inform your workforce;
   ■   manage any episodes of ULDs;
   ■   carry out regular checks on programme effectiveness.

5   Each stage is considered in a separate section of the guidance. An overview of the approach is shown in Figure 1. (see also paragraph 30)

6   Appendices 1-4 include the following:

   ■   Appendix 1: illustrates real life examples where the risks of ULDs have been managed.
   ■   Appendix 2: provides practical help with risk assessment and contains a Risk Assessment Filter and Worksheets and suggestions for reducing the risk.
   ■   Appendix 3: gives background information on medical aspects of ULDs.
   ■   Appendix 4: sets out the range of legal duties which apply to the prevention of ULDs.

7   Vibration is included in this document where it contributes to the development of ULDs, but the guidance does not cover all aspects of the prevention of vibration-induced illnesses, such as vibration white finger.[3,4] In addition, the risks of upper limb

disorders due to Display Screen Equipment (DSE) use are covered by the DSE regulations, and separate HSE guidance is specifically available on this topic.[5,6] Duty holders must comply with the DSE regulations; however this ULD guidance may be used to provide supplementary information.

Upper limb disorders: Understand the issues and commit to action

Understand the issues
Commit to action

5

CALDERDALE LIBRARIES

- Is the risk of ULDs recognised in your workplace?
- Is management committed to preventing or minimising the risk of ULDs?
- Are there adequate management systems and policies to support the commitment?

Understand the issues

What are upper limb disorders?

8   The phrase 'upper limb disorders' is a general label which is used to refer to a range of medical conditions which can be caused or made worse by work. There are a number of common terms which are also in use to describe the same conditions, of which the most well known is 'repetitive strain injury'. Other lesser known terms are 'cumulative trauma disorder', or 'occupational overuse syndrome'. These common terms can be misleading with regard to the many factors which can contribute to the onset of the conditions, and for this reason the more general description of 'upper limb disorders' is used in this guidance.

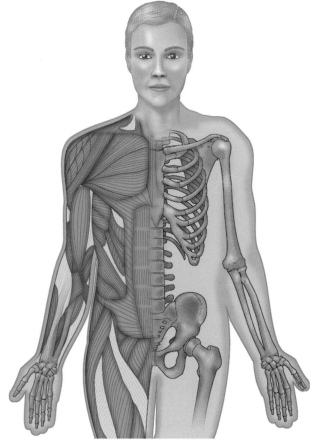

9   The term upper limb refers to:

- the part of the body: the arm and hand, covering a region extending from the tips of the fingers to the shoulder and extending into the neck;
- the tissues: the soft-tissues, muscles and connective tissues (tendons and ligaments) and the bony structures, as well as the skin, along with the circulatory and nerve supply to the limb.

Figure 2

10   The term 'disorder' refers to the clinical effects produced by underlying changes in the tissues. These comprise symptoms such as pain, experienced by the person, and signs which are abnormalities, eg in the appearance of the limb, which may be apparent to the person or may only be found on examination by a doctor. These clinical effects are accompanied by functional changes, eg a reduction in the ability to use the affected part of the limb and are often associated with a restriction in the range or speed of movement. Strength and sensation may also be affected. Although the clinical and functional effects are confined to the limb itself, their presence will often lead to a reduction in an individuals' assessment of their general health and to a reduction in their quality of life.

11   Upper limb disorders can be described by the part of the body affected, or by the presumed pathological mechanism. There are common terms for many of the individual conditions, such as 'tennis elbow' and 'frozen shoulder'. A simple guide to the more common upper limb disorders is contained in Appendix 3.

12   Pain is a common symptom of ULDs but the experience of pain in the upper limb is also common amongst the general population. Therefore, feeling pain in the upper limb is not in itself an indication of the presence of an ULD, and such symptoms may be difficult to attribute to work with any certainty.

13   Pain can also be experienced in the form of stiffness or soreness of the muscles accompanied by temporary fatigue. These symptoms are comparable to those following unaccustomed exertion where no permanent pathological condition results. Full recovery usually occurs after appropriate rest.

14   At any one time it is possible to experience symptoms in the upper limb which result from a number of different causes. This guidance is primarily concerned with ULDs for which there is evidence to believe that the conditions can be caused by, or made worse by work activity.

Are all upper limb disorders work-related?

15   The simple answer is no, but experience has shown that ULDs are often directly linked to workplace activities or if due to a non-work cause, made worse by work.

16   It is important to recognise that the musculoskeletal system is well suited to producing repeated motions at low force levels. Undesirable forces may, however, be imposed on muscles, tendons and joints by some job demands and working practices. Such stresses are usually within the physical capability or strength of the tissues, provided the forces are of short duration and rest periods are adequate. Prolonged tissue loading caused by static posture or performance of very frequent exertions can, however, be harmful.

17   There are established associations between many types of ULDs and work tasks, or specific risk factors within these tasks.[7] Evidence comes from:

   ▪ anecdotal reports which have historically linked specific occupations and particular conditions;[8]
   ▪ clinical case studies and reporting schemes for occupational diseases;[9,10]
   ▪ workplace surveys of symptoms;[11]
   ▪ epidemiological reviews[7,12] and population surveys;[13,14]
   ▪ laboratory studies of the physiological impact of experimentally imposed physical stresses.[15,16,17]

18   The reviews of the epidemiological literature [7,18] provide good evidence of the associations between workplace risk factors and ULDs, particularly where workers are highly exposed to these risk factors.

19   Non-work activities, such as domestic activity and hobbies, may contain similar types of risk as are found in work activities. These tasks are generally not as repetitive, forceful, or prolonged as are work tasks. Also, the individual has a high degree of control as to when the activity can be temporarily stopped or abandoned altogether.

How big is the problem?

20   Musculoskeletal disorders are the most common work related ailment afflicting the general population in Great Britain. They account for more than half of all self-reported occupational ill health (more than 1 million cases).[13] These problems are not confined to particular jobs or sectors and are found throughout most manufacturing and service industries.

21   Based on a household survey done in 1995, an estimated 506 000 people were suffering from a musculoskeletal disorder which affected the upper limbs or neck.

22   An estimated minimum 4.2 million working days were lost in Britain due to musculoskeletal disorders affecting the upper limbs or neck in 1995, with each affected employee taking, on average, 13 days off work.[14] Costs to employers of musculoskeletal disorders of the upper limbs or neck were estimated to be at least £200 million.

What types of job carry particular risks?

23   Evidence gathered over recent years shows that ULDs are not confined to any one

particular group of workers or industrial activity, but are widespread in the workforce. The following list of groups which have reported high levels of arm pain illustrates this point. A common feature of the jobs is that their tasks have recognised risk factors:

- assembly line workers;
- cleaning and domestic staff;
- construction workers;
- garment machinists;
- hairdressers;
- meat and poultry processors;
- mushroom pickers;
- pottery workers;
- secretaries/temps;
- textile workers.

24   This list is not exhaustive, and there are many other jobs that carry a risk of ULDs. Similarly, the presence of jobs on this list does not imply that the risk of injury to these workers cannot be adequately controlled.

Why should I be concerned?

25   If work which carries the risk of ULDs is not managed properly then the consequences are seen in:

- the human cost of pain and suffering experienced by employees and their families through ill health;
- loss of earnings;
- loss of the ability to work;
- problems in quality control and productivity;
- decrease in efficiency;
- sickness absence;
- costs of staff replacement and training;
- the risk of litigation;
- the risk of bad publicity;
- a rise in insurance premiums and costs of compensation to injured workers.

26   Any warning signs may be the 'tip of the iceberg'. One person with symptoms may mean there are numerous other workers also exposed to risk factors, and who are in the process of developing a disorder.

What are my legal responsibilities?

27   There are general duties on all employers under the Health and Safety at Work etc Act 1974[19] and the Management of Health and Safety at Work Regulations 1999[20] which require the risks of ULDs to be addressed. These, and other legal responsibilities are outlined in Appendix 4.

28   ULDs have also been the subject of much civil litigation over the past twenty years.[21] Although the legal process has sometimes appeared inconsistent there is no doubt that the employer's duty of care towards their employees with respect to ULDs is now well established in the civil courts. This civil law duty runs parallel to the employer's statutory responsibility under health and safety legislation.

Commit to action

29   Realising that ULDs may be a risk within, and to, your business is not enough. It is essential to turn that awareness and understanding into a commitment to take action to manage the risks. The framework in Figure 1 outlines seven stages which form a sound basis for developing an effective programme for the management of ULD risks.

30   The stages are as follows:

- **Understand the issues and commit to action:** Management and workers should have an understanding of ULDs and be committed to action on prevention. This commitment may be expressed through positive leadership on the topic, by generating an effective health and safety policy on ULDs and by having appropriate systems in place. These actions will help to promote a positive health and safety culture in the workplace.

- **Create the right organisational environment:** The organisational environment should foster active worker participation and involvement, have clear and open lines of communication and encourage partnership working in the next five steps. This will involve developing the competencies of workers, supervisors and managers for their differing roles.

- **Assess the risks of ULDs in your workplace:** A core feature of the management programme is to assess the risk of ULDs. It needs to be done in a systematic way by managers and workers so that the main risks in the workplace can be identified and prioritised for action. As risks are potentially widespread, simple checks, including a filter questionnaire can be used to identify jobs which require a more detailed assessment.

- **Reduce the risks of ULDs:** Once risks have been assessed and prioritised a coherent process of risk reduction should be undertaken using an ergonomics approach. Possible risks should be reduced or eliminated at source. Implementation should include workforce participation as this is known to lead to better solutions and more effective, sustained changes.

■ **Educate and inform your workforce:** To enable participation and involvement of the workforce and for individuals to assume their proper responsibilities, provision of education and information is vital. Training will support all aspects of the management programme, and should be considered as an on going activity and not as a 'one-off' task.

■ **Manage any episodes of ULDs:** It is important to have a system to manage any episodes of ULDs. Employees should be encouraged to identify any symptoms and to report them before they become persistent. Managers need to respond quickly by reviewing risks and introducing more effective controls, if necessary. They also need to reassure employees that reporting of symptoms will not prejudice their job or position. Early medical management can stop established cases from deteriorating and also help the process of return to work.

■ **Carry out regular checks on programme effectiveness:** To ensure that this programme continues to work properly over time regular checks of effectiveness should be carried out. This will help to ensure that controls on ULD risks remain effective and will allow you to progressively improve their effectiveness.

Management commitment

31   If this programme of control is to work effectively then it is important to demonstrate management commitment to the whole process. Effective management of occupational health risks is characterised by:

■   visible senior management involvement;
■   open management style;
■   good communications which engender ownership of problems (ie personal responsibility and participation);
■   an appropriate balance between health and safety and production goals.

Supporting policies and systems

32   A clear policy for the management of ULDs sets the direction for the organisation and means that people throughout the organisation, however large or small it is, will know that the prevention of ULDs is an issue which has to be addressed in all stages of business planning, both for day-to-day operations and in the longer term.

33   The framework in Figure 1 and the guidance in the following sections are a means to turn your intentions into reality and to keep these intentions under scrutiny.

Create the right organisational environment

Participation and involvement
Communication
Competence
Allocation of responsibilities

> - Is worker participation actively sought and valued?
> - Are safety representatives involved?
> - Are all departments aware of the contribution they can make?
> - Is competence ensured?
> - Have you allocated responsibilities?

34   The effective management of ULDs requires senior management commitment. In addition, it needs the presence in the organisation of shared and interlinked beliefs, attitudes and behaviours that allow the management of risks to proceed effectively. These elements make up what has been referred to as the health and safety climate or culture. Key features crucial to developing a positive environment for dealing with ULD problems include:

- participation and involvement;
- communication;
- competence;
- allocation of responsibilities.

Participation and involvement

35   Involving staff in the planning and organisational processes can be an important way of increasing the likelihood of success of your risk control strategy. Workers have first-hand knowledge and an almost unique understanding about particular aspects of the tasks they perform. It may however be important to provide education and training on ULDs before expecting employees to contribute fully to the process of assessment and control. Key individuals are Safety Representatives as they provide an effective channel for communication with the workforce they represent and they can use their functions to provide a 'reality check' to ensure that the proposed control measures might actually work. The Health and Safety (Consultation with Employees) Regulations 1996,[22] Safety Representatives and Safety Committees Regulations 1996,[23] and the Offshore Installations (Safety Representatives and Safety Committees) Regulations 1989[24] require you to consult with your employees on their health and safety at work. This would extend to actions you intend to take to tackle ULDs. Further information about employee participation can be found in *Development of a framework for participatory ergonomics*[25] and also *Handle with care - assessing musculoskeletal risks in the chemical industry.*[26]

36   A supportive company culture and openness will be important factors in ensuring that the adverse effects of ULDs are not 'hidden' from management. Encouraging early reporting of work related aches and pains to supervisors or line managers, and in turn to the occupational health service (if you have one available) can provide significant benefits

for both the employee and the company. One of the main difficulties with reporting is the fear of the outcome, eg possibly being declared unfit for work. This is where an open, positive culture becomes important. Employees ought to feel safe to report aches and pains early in their onset.

Communication

37   Good communication will ensure that staff members in every department of your business are aware of the risks of ULDs and what they can do to help reduce them. Product design staff will influence the details of the manufacturing process and the decisions of marketing staff will determine the nature of the packaging required. Purchasing departments will control the sourcing of the equipment used and general management will determine terms and conditions including working schedules. In some cases, factors which influence these risks may be controlled at a distance in a parent organisation. A range of methods should be used to ensure that everyone is kept informed of how their roles can impact on other workers and also the company's programme on the prevention of ULDs. These are likely to include seminars, meetings, posters and articles in the house journal or newsletter. The internet also provides some useful websites, some of which are included in the Further Information section.

38   An open system of communication should provide opportunities to distribute information to employees and also opportunities for feedback. This can be informal (eg to supervisors) or more structured, for example through regular surveys. If complaints occur they should be investigated.

Competence

39   It is important that people are competent to prevent ULDs within their technical areas of responsibility. Health and safety training is important, paying particular attention to the risk factors for ULDs and how these may be avoided. Some groups of staff may require specialised training, eg in the application of ergonomic principles, evaluation of workplace changes or the recognition of upper limb health complaints.

40   The need for competence also extends to areas such as the operation of recruitment and placement procedures and systems to identify training needs when work practices and technologies change. Staff development systems can be used to ensure that individuals have access to the training they require, and their operation can form part of the regular checks on programme effectiveness.

Allocation of responsibilities

41　As many people will have a role in your programme to prevent ULDs, it is important to be clear about who is responsible for what functions. For example, supervisors who understand the risks can take an active role in helping to control them, and in encouraging staff to report any problems. You may need to set up systems to deal with any problems which may occur, to ensure an early response to them.

42　Setting objectives for your organisation, with clear roles and accountabilities will help keep you on target. You may be able to use benchmarking as a way of checking progress, eg between departments or with neighbouring businesses.

Assess the risk of ULDs in your workplace

What is an ergonomics approach?
Identifying problem tasks
Risk assessment
ULD risk factors

> - Are any ULD hazards identified through simple checks?
> - Are risk factors for ULDs present?
>   Repetition, working posture, force, duration of exposure, working environment, psychosocial factors, individual differences,

43   Assessing the risk associated with ULDs involves two major steps namely:

- identifying problem tasks; and
- risk assessment.

44   An example of a method for tackling the above two steps can be found in Appendix 2.

45   In order to be able to get the most benefit from the process, you and your workforce need to be able to work together to identify, assess and control the risk of ULDs. This process should involve an ergonomics approach and should include the participation of workers.

What is an ergonomics approach?

46   Ergonomics (or human factors), is concerned with ensuring work is designed to take account of people, their capabilities and limitations. Its objective is to optimise health, safety and productivity. An ergonomics approach is the most effective way of dealing with ULD problems. This is because it encourages you to take account of all the relevant parts of the work system and requires worker participation.

Identifying problem tasks

47   There are two main approaches you can use to identify if you have a problem in your workplace. Firstly managers and workers can look for any signs of problems or symptoms amongst the workforce. Secondly, you can observe work tasks themselves to see if risk factors for ULDs are present. This can be done using a simple initial assessment of risks such as the risk filter approach found in Appendix 2. Sources of information that may help include expert advice, industry standards and legislative standards.

Warning signs

48   Warning signs can indicate the presence of hazards relating to ULDs. Signs of existing

ULD problems can include:

- injury and illness records;
- jobs which workers are reluctant to do;
- jobs where workers complain of discomfort;
- workers having made adaptations to workstations, tools or chairs;
- workers requesting to be re-deployed or taken off a job;
- splints or bandages being worn, and/or;
- use of painkillers.

Figure 3

49   Paragraphs 120-128 outline other ways of monitoring the number of workers who are experiencing upper limb pain or discomfort.

Risk Filter

50   A detailed assessment of every job could be a major undertaking and might be an unnecessary effort. To help identify situations where a detailed assessment is necessary, a Filter for an initial screening of tasks has been devised. Where the Filter identifies several risk factors in combination, the risk of ULDs is likely to be greater. A copy of the Risk Filter and instructions for use can be found in Appendix 2.

Risk assessment

51   Once you have identified that certain tasks may be creating a risk of ULDs (by looking for signs and symptoms and using the risk filter), a more detailed risk assessment should be conducted, involving managers and workers, in order to ascertain the likelihood and severity of risk. ULD assessment worksheets that can assist in recognising and recording risk factors, can be found in Appendix 2.

The risk assessment process

52   A job often consists of series of tasks. Performing your risk assessment can be simplified by thinking in terms of these tasks and their subsidiary elements. To illustrate this point,

Figure 4 describes the job of a process worker that consists of three different tasks on an assembly line:

- station 1: attaching a handle;
- station 2: grinding, and;
- station 3: packing.

53   As can be seen in this example, these tasks can also be further broken down into elements, which are distinct sequences of movement within the task.

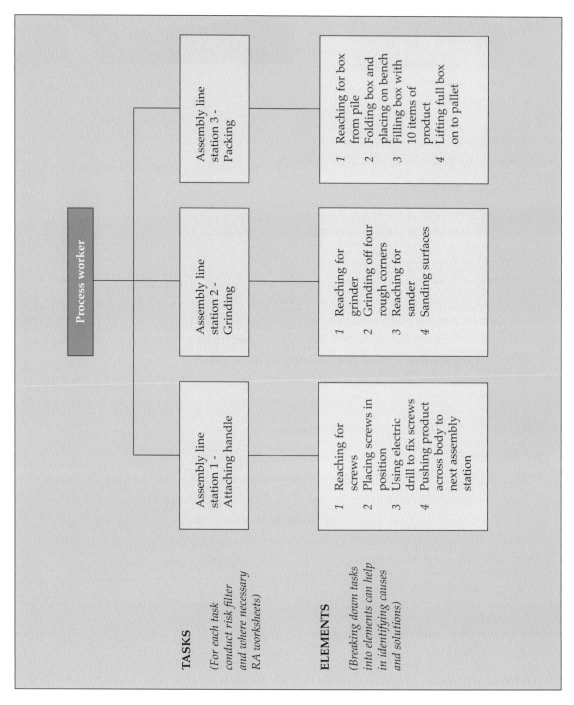

Figure 4 **The tasks and elements of a process worker's role**

54 Looking at task elements can help both in identifying the causes of risks and in devising potential solutions. For example, in the case of the process worker the risk filter might identify the task of attaching a handle (station 1) as posing a possible risk. The more detailed assessment using the worksheet would identify repeated use of a pinch grip when picking up and positioning the screws (elements 1 and 2), and awkward arm posture out to the side of the body when drilling (element 3). When considering the task in this way it is easier to link the risks to particular actions or operations, which then helps when considering risk reduction measures.

55 In this case better positioning of the assembly line in relation to the worker, and re-orientating the objects will reduce the risk to the right arm and shoulder. Reducing the duration spent on the task and introducing more frequent breaks will reduce the risk associated with using the pinch grip.

56 Remember to consider whether workers perform a number of potentially risky tasks (ie that have been highlighted by the risk filter), in a given shift. If this is the case, it is essential that your risk assessment considers the overall impact of performing the combination of tasks in your risk assessment. In practice, this would usually mean that a separate filter and risk assessment worksheet would be filled out for each task, and that the completed worksheets would be considered in combination when deciding on the overall level of risk for those workers. Detailed instructions for the risk filter and risk assessment worksheets can be found in Appendix 2.

57 Other risk assessment tools are available.[27,28,29,30] These range from standardised or quantitative tools that are usually required to be undertaken by a competent person, to simple checklists. Engaging a competent person may be appropriate for more complex risk assessments.

ULD risk factors

58 Risk factors can be thought of as task, environment, or worker-related within an ergonomic approach. The principal ULD risk factors are:

Task-related factors	■ repetition; ■ working postures; ■ force; ■ duration of exposure.
Environment-related factors	■ working environment; ■ psychosocial factors.
Worker-related factors	■ individual differences.

59   Each of these risk factors, including their definitions and why they create the risk of ULDs, will be discussed in more detail in the following paragraphs.

60   Risk factors commonly interact with each other in creating the overall risk of ULDs. For example, the task of gripping a heavy power tool with a large handle for six hours would result in an awkward, forceful gripping posture and exposure to vibration over a prolonged period. Therefore working postures, duration, force and working environment are all risk factors for injury in this task.

61   In contrast, if this task was only done for a short period in each shift, the risk of injury may not be high. This is despite the fact that the risk factors of working postures; force and vibration are still present.

62   Generally, there is an increased risk of injury when there are a number of risk factors acting in combination. However, one risk factor acting alone can create an unacceptable risk of injury if it is sufficiently great in magnitude, frequency or duration.

Repetition

63   Work is repetitive when it requires the same muscle groups to be used over and over again during the working day or when it requires frequent movements to be performed for prolonged periods.

Figure 5

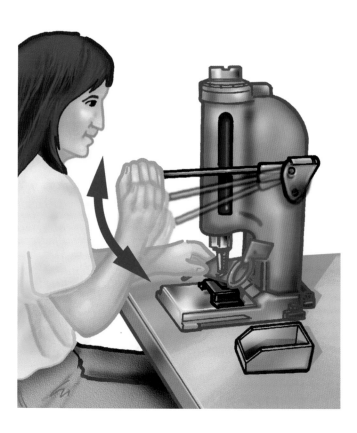

64   Rapid or prolonged repetition may not allow sufficient time for recovery and can cause muscle fatigue due to depletion of energy and a build up of metabolic waste materials. Repeated loading of soft tissues is also associated with inflammation, degeneration and microscopic changes. Fast movements and acceleration require high muscle forces.

Working posture

65 Working postures can increase the risk of injury when they are awkward and/or held for prolonged periods in a static or fixed position.

Figure 6

Awkward postures

66 An awkward posture is where a part of the body (eg a limb joint) is used well beyond its neutral position. A neutral position is where the trunk and head are upright, the arms are by the side of the body, forearms are hanging straight or at a right angle to the upper arm, and the hand is in the handshake position. For example, when a person's arm is hanging straight down with the elbow by the side of the body, the shoulder is in a neutral position. However, when employees are performing overhead work (eg repairing equipment or accessing objects from a high shelf) their shoulders are far from the neutral position.

67 When awkward postures are adopted, additional muscular effort is needed to maintain body positions, as muscles are less efficient at the extremes of the joint range. Resulting friction and compression of soft tissue structures can also lead to injury.

Static postures

68 Static postures occur when a part of the body is held in a particular position for extended periods of time without the soft tissues being allowed to relax. When holding a box, for example, it is likely that the hands and arms are in a static posture.

69 Static loadings restrict blood flow to the muscles and tendons resulting in less opportunity for recovery and metabolic waste removal. Muscles held in static postures fatigue very quickly.

70   In both the above types of posture (awkward and static), the risk of ULDs will be related to the number of times the posture is repeated, the amount of force required, and/or the length of time it is held. As with all the risk factors for ULDs, the impact of the working posture needs to be understood in relation to other risk factors.

Force

71   Force can be applied to the muscles, tendons, nerves and joints of the upper limb by:

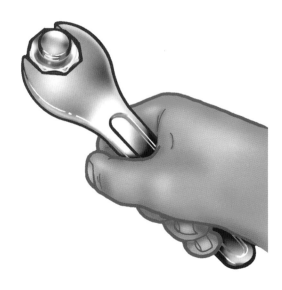

Figure 7

   ■   handling heavy objects when performing tasks, ie an external load;

   ■   fast movement or excessive force generated by the muscles of the body – often to be transmitted to an external load, eg trying to undo a stiff bolt;

   ■   local force and stress from items coming into contact with parts of the upper limb, such as the handle of a pair of pliers digging into the palm of the hand.

72   The level of force that is generated by the muscles is affected by a number of factors including:

   ■   working posture: the level of muscular effort required increases when a part of the body is in an awkward posture;

   ■   the size and weight of objects being handled;

   ■   the speed of movement: as extra force is needed at the beginning and end of fast movements such as hammering; and

   ■   vibrating tools or equipment: as operators need to use increased grip force in working with vibrating equipment.

73   Use of excessive force can lead to fatigue and if sustained, to injury, either through a single-event strain injury or through the cumulative effect of the repeated use of such force. Local force and stress can also cause direct pressure on the nerves and/or blood vessels and increase the risk of discomfort and injury.

Force in gripping

74   The need to grip raw materials, product or tools is a potential risk factor if excessive force is used. The amount of force required to grip can be influenced by the type of grip used, the posture of the wrist, exposure to cold and vibration and the effects of wearing gloves.

75   The force required to grip objects is also dependent upon the material or item being gripped. For example, a screwdriver handle with a flexible grip requires less force when being used than one with a harder handle. The size of the object being gripped can also affect the force required. For example, pliers with too wide or too narrow a span will be more difficult to grip.

76   Muscle force is greatest when a power grip (eg gripping a handle in the palm with fingers and thumb) is used as, this allows a large surface area of the hand to be utilised. The strongest grip strength occurs when the wrist is close to the 'handshake' position and is slightly bent upwards.

Duration of exposure

77   Duration refers to the length of time for which a task is performed. It includes the length of time that the task is undertaken in each shift, plus the number of working days the task is performed (eg four hours per day, five days per week). Duration is an important concept in assessing the risk of musculoskeletal disorders.

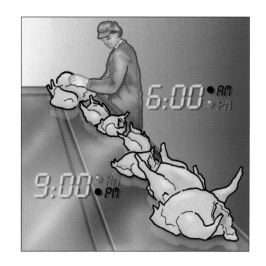

78   It is generally accepted that many types of upper limb disorders are cumulative in nature. Therefore, when duration time is increased the risk of injury is increased. This is because when parts of the body undertake work for periods without rest, there may be insufficient time for recovery. Consequently,

Figure 8

time for the individual's body to recover from a specific task or tasks is important.

79   Short exposures are unlikely to create significant risk of injury, except where the task is exceptionally demanding and/or the worker has not been allowed to build up to its demands over a period of time. This can occur after return to work from holidays or with an increase in work pace.

Working Environment

80   Working environment refers to aspects of the physical work environment that can increase the risk of ULDs. This includes factors such as vibration, cold and lighting.

Vibration

81   Exposure to hand-arm vibration results from the use of hand-held/guided power tools and equipment or fixed machinery such as bench grinders where the workpiece is held by the worker. Vibration can increase the risk of ULDs and is known to cause vibration white finger and carpal tunnel syndrome, loss of sense of touch or temperature, painful joints and loss of grip strength. Information about the dose (ie vibration magnitude and exposure time) of vibration is needed in order to accurately assess the risk. Further information on vibration can be found in *Hand-arm vibration*[3], ISO 5349-2[4] and Appendix 3.

Figure 9

Cold

82   Working in cold temperatures, handling cold products or having cold air blowing on parts of the body can place additional demands on the body as well as possibly requiring the use of personal protective equipment (which can compound the risk by requiring additional force to grip). Exposure to cold can result in decreased blood flow to the hands and upper limbs, decreased sensation and dexterity, decreased maximum grip strength and increased muscle activity (which is part of the body's natural response to being cold).

Figure 10

Lighting

83   The visual demands of the task are an important consideration, since a worker's posture can be largely dictated by what they need to see. Dim light, shadow, glare or flickering light can encourage workers to adopt a bent neck and poor shoulder postures in order to see their work, thereby exacerbating the effects of other risk factors. Further information on lighting can be found in Lighting at work.[31]

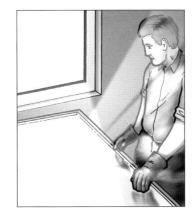

Figure 11

Psychosocial factors

84   Physical risk factors exert their harmful influence through physiological and biomechanical loading of the upper limb. Of equal importance is the large body of work showing that a worker's psychological response to work and workplace conditions has an important influence on health in general and musculoskeletal health in particular; that is, work as experienced by workers. These are referred to as psychosocial risk factors. They include the design, organisation and management of work and the overall social environment in general (the context of work) and also the specific impact of job factors (the content of work). It is very likely that physical and psychosocial risk factors combine and that the greatest benefit will be achieved when both are identified and controlled. Many of the effects of these psychosocial factors occur via stress-related processes which include direct biochemical and physiological changes. Also included are instances where individuals try to cope with stressful demands with behaviours that, in the long term, may be detrimental to health. An example would be where an individual, because of high workload or deadlines, foregoes the rest breaks to which they are entitled.

85   Psychosocial risk factors are common in sectors where upper limb disorders occur[13]. Important aspects of work design include the amount of control people have in their jobs, the level of work demands, the variety of tasks that they have to carry out and the support they receive from supervisors and co-workers. Many jobs are not well designed and include some or all of the following undesirable features where:

- workers have little control over their work and work methods (including shift patterns);
- tasks require high levels of attention and concentration especially in conditions where the worker has little control over the allocation of effort to the task;

- workers are unable to make full use of their skills;
- they are not, as a rule, involved in making decisions that affect them;
- they are expected to carry out repetitive, monotonous tasks exclusively;
- work is machine or system paced (and may be monitored inappropriately);
- work demands are perceived as excessive;
- payment systems encourage working too quickly or without breaks;
- work systems limit opportunities for social interaction;
- high levels of effort are not balanced by sufficient reward (resources, remuneration, self-esteem, status);

As with physical risk factors, psychosocial issues are best addressed with full consultation and involvement of the workforce.

Individual differences

86 All individuals are different and for biological reasons there may be some people who are more or less likely to develop an ULD. Individual differences may also have implications for employees reporting ULD type conditions. Where an ergonomic approach is followed, this should ensure that tasks are within the capabilities of the entire workforce. Some factors *may* increase the risk of developing symptoms and should be considered in the management programme. These include:

- new employees may need time to acquire the necessary work skills and/or rate of work;
- difference in competence and skills;
- workers of varying body sizes, ie height, reach etc. This can lead to adopting poor postures when working at shared workstations;
- vulnerable groups, eg older, younger workers and new or expectant mothers;[32]
- health status and disability;
- individual attitudes or characteristics that may affect compliance with safe working practices or reporting of symptoms.

Reduce the risk of ULDs

> ■ Have you prioritised your actions to control the risks of ULDs?
> ■ Have you looked for 'higher order' solutions?
> ■ Have you utilised an ergonomics approach?
> ■ Have you implemented solutions?

87 Having assessed the work to determine the likelihood and scale of the risks associated with each of the relevant tasks (and the tasks in combination where applicable), you must implement controls in order to reduce these risks as far as is reasonably practicable.

88 Prioritise actions so that, for example, serious risks affecting a number of employees are tackled before an isolated complaint of minor discomfort.

Look for 'higher order' solutions

89 A hierarchical approach to risk reduction and control should be followed where priority is given to elimination of risk at source. Firstly, consider if it is reasonably practicable to eliminate the hazard, eg by redesign of the work task, by substitution or replacement of tools or components, or through automation of the task. In some cases it may be possible to isolate the risks at source by engineering controls or protective measures, eg by shielding the worker from draughts or by preventing exposure to vibration. Where these are not viable, the lowest order in the hierarchy of controls is to minimise risk by designing suitable systems of work, using PPE if appropriate and to provide training.

Using an ergonomics approach

90 As in risk assessment, an ergonomics approach is important in developing your interventions to reduce risk. A participative approach to solution finding is considered to be the most effective method for intervention development.[18] Interventions may involve changes to the task, the working environment, or the individual (or work group) or to all of these. Research has shown that interventions that take account of all these aspects are more effective in reducing risk:

■ Changes to the work **task(s)** may include redesign of the workstation and work equipment. It may include the provision of appropriate furniture, equipment or tools that have been matched to the needs of the workers and the task. Job rotation or automation may be beneficial in reducing ULD risks.
■ Changes to the **environment** could include modifications to the thermal conditions, vibration exposure or lighting levels. Changes to influence psychosocial factors may

be required. A review of the work organisation and structure such as reduction of work hours or changes to scheduling of breaks, or modifying pacing or incentive schemes may also be helpful.

■ Training and provision of information to **individuals** or work groups may also be needed to support other changes.

Basic principles in implementing solutions

91 Risks can be removed or reduced through systematic attention to some or all of the factors mentioned previously. Some helpful principles are:

■ great benefit often results from simple and low cost interventions (eg changes in working height) which are generally more practical and easier to implement;

■ consider a number of possible solutions, preferably trying them out on a small scale before deciding on one to implement;

■ employees can be especially good at devising effective and practical improvement measures;

■ check that any changes do not create new health and safety risks elsewhere;

■ successful implementation often requires the involvement of all employees from the top level downwards. Even sound ergonomic solutions may not be successful if they are imposed. Involving workers in problem solving and the implementation processes, gives an enhanced sense of ownership of the solutions and may create a greater commitment to their effective implementation;

■ in large, geographically spread organisations, incorporate short-term local initiatives into the company's overall health and safety strategy;

■ refer to case studies from other sources, eg from trade associations or the Internet, for ideas concerning best practice solutions.

Individual differences

92 All tasks should be designed so they can be undertaken without creating a risk of ULDs. There is no scientifically valid screening test which can predict the future development of ULDs in an individual. Placement procedures should take account of the risk assessment, job requirements and the individual differences outlined in the previous section.

93 New employees, particularly young workers, and those returning to work from a holiday, sickness or injury, may need to be introduced to a slower rate of production than the existing 'workforce', followed by a gradual increase in pace. This works best, for example, by only working for a limited time per day at production speed, increasing as appropriate. Introducing newcomers at a slower pace enables them to develop good work practices before having to concentrate on working fast and helps them to assimilate

training more effectively: ideally, early training should be done 'off-line'. Regulation 12 in the Management of Health and Safety at Work Regulations 1999[20] details requirements concerning new employees.

Suggestions for reducing the risk

94   Some examples of approaches that may be useful for reducing the risk of ULDs are listed in Appendix 2.

Other guidance on solutions

95   HSE has produced a number of publications that provide guidance on reducing workplace musculoskeletal disorders. This includes guidance based on case studies[33, 34] as well as some that is industry-specific. Information can also be found on the HSE, and some other websites. See 'further information' for sources.

96   If you are unsure of how to approach implementing changes within the workplace, you may wish to consider seeking specialist advice from an ergonomist or other workplace health and safety consultant.

After implementation

97   Finally, it is important to monitor the situation to make sure solutions are still effective at a later date (particularly where their success depends on some form of learning or behaviour change). Keep abreast of new developments (eg when new machinery or staff are introduced into the workplace or when other alternative risk control measures are developed). Monitoring and reviewing are explained in paragraphs 120-132.

Educate and inform your workforce

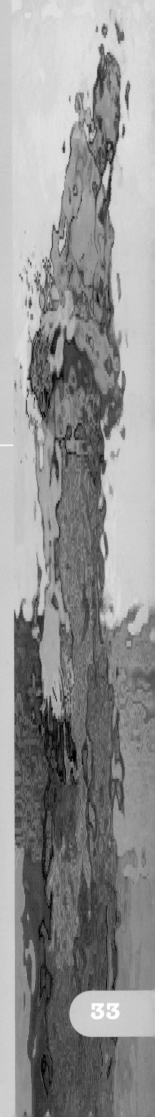

> - Have you educated and informed your workforce to help prevention?
> - Have you involved safety representatives in communicating information about ULD risk factors?
> - What steps have you taken to ensure that training reinforces safe working practices and control measures?

98   Education and training are complementary to all other aspects of your programme for the prevention of ULDs and indeed are critical to its success. Informing staff about signs and symptoms of ULDs, risk factors, control measures and the need for early reporting and action will improve the overall effectiveness of your programme and will encourage employees to become actively involved in identifying and controlling ULD risks.

Training as a control measure

99   Training should not be relied on as the primary means of controlling the risk of ULDs. Influencing the way workers perform tasks through training is an essential part of risk control, but relying on this alone has been shown to have limited success in prevention. Training should ideally complement other higher order controls that have already been implemented (ie redesign of the work task, substitution or replacement of tools or components, isolating the risk at the source etc). It can be very beneficial to involve employees in the development and presentation of training.

Who should receive education?

100   All workers, supervisors and managers should receive education on ULDs to enable them to identify the early warning signs of potential ULD risk factors. Education should also extend to purchasing staff, engineers, maintenance and support staff, particularly where they are involved in specifying, designing or modifying work equipment in order to increase their awareness of ergonomic issues and ULD risk factors.

What should training cover?

101   Training can be designed both to raise general awareness of ULD issues and to address the specific needs of a particular job or task. General training should aim to:

- increase awareness and knowledge of ULD issues/problems in the workplace;

- reduce the likelihood of ULD problems by providing adequate information:
  - recognition of symptoms of ULDs (see Appendix 3);
  - risk factors present in the workplace;
  - safe working methods;
  - correct operation of control measures;
  - the importance of procedures for the early reporting of ULD symptoms.

102 Task-specific training should consider ULD risk factors associated with the job in greater detail. Such training should include a review of risk factors related to tasks and safe working methods for that particular task. Any specific control measures associated with the job, including personal protective equipment should also be covered.

Making training more effective

103 Training that involves no more than sitting with an experienced employee who does not have appropriate understanding of ULDs is unlikely to be satisfactory since bad habits and practices can easily be passed on to the new employee. When attempting to alter worker behaviour, programmes will need to consider:

- adverse traditional methods and ingrained habits;
- production pressures;
- any perception that new methods are difficult or time consuming;
- any lack of understanding of risk factors for ULDs;
- situations where improvements in job methods may be constrained by poor workplace layout, materials, equipment and/or job design;
- employee involvement. This is fundamental to the success of any training programme. Employers should promote participation by encouraging discussion, asking employees for suggestions and comments on training issues and, where appropriate, involving employees in the presentation of training material;
- the role of safety representatives in promoting safe working practices and reinforcing training messages;
- the need to provide opportunities for immediate practice and feedback so as to correct performance and to ensure that skill levels can be maintained following training. Principles covered in training sessions should be reinforced by supervisors, safety representatives and peers on a regular basis;
- the need for periodic refresher training for all employees.

Evaluation and follow up

104 Periodic evaluation of your training programmes should be undertaken as part of a

general review of your ULD prevention programme. Employees should be involved in this process, particularly safety representatives and supervisors, who can assess the impact and effectiveness of the training offered. Training should also be reviewed when there are changes in:

- workplace layouts, task design or work organisation or the introduction of new work equipment;
- work practices or control measures;
- reported injury levels in other workplaces in the industry, or in workplaces with similar jobs.

Manage any episodes of ULDs

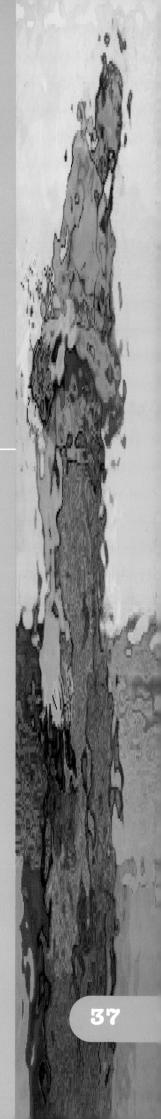

Reporting and recording
Referral
Diagnosis and return to work
Surveillance

- Have you implemented and supported a system for early reporting of ULDs?
- Do you actively look for symptoms of ULDs?
- Have you arranged for occupational health provision?
- Do you have systems in place for employees returning to work after an ULD?

105   Adequate control of risk factors will go a long way to prevent the occurrence of ULDs. Due to individual differences in the body's response to stresses it is not possible to ensure that every possible episode of ULDs will always be prevented. It is necessary, therefore, to have a system in place to manage any reports or cases of ULDs that arise in the workforce. The approach to managing these complaints is broadly similar whether they are thought to have been caused by work activity, been made worse by the work or are largely unrelated to particular work tasks.

Reporting and recording

106   Individuals will vary in their willingness to report early symptoms of ULDs. It is important to maintain a climate in which early reporting of symptoms is regarded positively and this will be encouraged if managers and safety representatives both emphasise the benefits of such early detection of possible harm. Education on possible symptoms and signs, who to see in the company and what help to expect should be provided to all employees where there is a residual risk of ULDs. Employees should be advised to have any relevant symptoms recorded in the company 'accident book'. Any first aid provided should also be documented.

107   If symptoms are such that continuing to work does not make them worse, then it may be enough to provide the worker with reassurance, advice on risk factors, and to review the individual's work tasks with them.

108   If continuing to work at the same job causes symptoms to get worse or become prolonged, or if the person was concerned about the nature of the symptoms then it would be appropriate to obtain further advice by means of a referral to a health professional. A diagnostic support aid for ULDs has been developed and is likely to be of benefit to General Practitioners (GPs) and other health professionals.[35] If symptoms are aggravated by a person's current job it is advisable to look for alternative work that they can do, even if this is quite different from their normal duties. This can prevent the need for sickness absence and allow for recovery time before return to their normal duties.

Referral

109 One way to obtain health advice is by referral to an occupational health service, either on or off site. Appendix 3 contains more information on the scope of occupational health provision and how to access this. Access to an occupational health service will usually allow both the worker and their manager to be given appropriate advice with minimal delay. The individual will be advised on the nature of their complaint and any appropriate treatment and the manager can be advised whether the complaints are likely to have been related to work and the short term implications for continuing employment.

110 If an employee is off sick with what is believed to be a ULD then it is useful to make early contact with the person, for example a telephone call, to see what you can do to help their return to work. Appendix 3 lists a number of specific medical diagnoses to look out for if you are concerned about complaints of ULDs.

111 If you do not have access to an occupational health service then, with your employee's agreement and written consent, you can write to their GP asking for a report which may help you in managing the absence. However, any such communication has to comply with the principles detailed in the Access to Medical Reports Act, 1988.[36,37] The following points could be raised:

- the nature of the illness;
- whether the doctor thinks it is related to work;
- if treatment will be necessary and time required to access treatment;
- when a return to work may be expected;
- whether activity will need to be limited for a period after returning to work;
- if any long term effects are to be expected from the illness.

112 Appendix 3 provides further information on a range of possible treatments for ULDs.

Diagnosis and return to work

113 Receipt of a written diagnosis of an upper limb disorder may trigger a requirement to make a report to the relevant enforcing authority under The Reporting of Injuries, Diseases and Dangerous Occurrences Regulations (RIDDOR).[38,39,40] This requirement applies only to a small number of ULDs which arise in the course of specified work activities. Appendix 4 provides further details.

114 A number of ULDs are also prescribed under the Social Security (Industrial Injuries) (Prescribed Diseases) Regulations 1985.[41] At the time of writing, the list of ULDs which are Prescribed Diseases is the same as those which are reportable under RIDDOR.

Individuals diagnosed with such disorders should be advised that they might be entitled to benefit under the Industrial Injuries Scheme.

115 Confirmation of a case of an ULD should be taken as a prompt to consider whether existing risk assessments and controls are adequate. This is especially important if there are other previously reported cases.

116 The exact timing of an individual's return to work will depend on the medical advice which they receive which in turn will depend on the nature of the underlying disorder. It is often possible to return to work before symptoms have resolved, and, in some cases this may be advantageous.

117 You may also need to review your arrangements for occupational health advice to assist with the management of any further cases which may occur. This is particularly important in work where there is already existing evidence of upper limb complaints.

Surveillance

118 Health surveillance can be undertaken on either a voluntary or a statutory basis. The Approved Code of Practice for the Management of Health and Safety at Work Regulations[20] recommends that health surveillance is undertaken where certain criteria are met. One of these is access to a valid means of detecting the disease or condition of concern. At present it is not considered that valid techniques exist for the detection of changes which reliably indicate the early onset of specific upper limb disorders.

119 Valuable information can however be obtained from less precise measures such as reports of symptoms. It is good practice to put in place systems which allow individuals to make early reports of upper limb complaints. Where appropriate these can be supplemented by regular surveys of symptoms. Further information can be found in *Health surveillance at work*.[42]

Carry out regular checks on programme effectiveness

- Do you have systems in place to monitor and review your controls for ULDs?
- Do you have systems in place to monitor and review your ULD management programme?
- Are you aware of new developments/information?
- Do you aim for continuous improvement?

Why monitor or review?

120 In any management system it is important to check the effectiveness of your actions, and this is no less so in the prevention of ULDs. These checks can be considered at two levels:

- monitoring: which is the ongoing and regular appraisal of the procedures and systems which you have in place to control risk; and
- reviewing: which is a less frequent but more strategic activity which considers how well the overall controls are working and whether any changes might be beneficial and reasonably practicable.

Monitoring

121 Monitoring is an integral part of management and requires commitment, consultation and participation at all levels in the organisation in order to be fully effective. Monitoring generally involves recording trends in ULD symptoms and risk factors over time in order to assess the performance of existing control measures and to plan and implement new interventions.

122 Factors to consider in planning monitoring and reviewing systems include:

- method;
- frequency;
- when to monitor;
- costs and benefits.

123 The method and frequency of monitoring should be considered when initially planning and implementing control measures. The scale and extent of monitoring required will depend on the degree of risk and the relative costs and benefits of available methods. It is important that there is consultation with employees so that they are fully aware of the monitoring procedures which are in place.

Approaches to monitoring

124 There are two broad approaches to monitoring systems – passive and active monitoring. Table 1 compares the general features of each approach.

Table 1 **General features of passive and active monitoring**

Passive	Active
Uses existing information sources and methods	Active seeking of information about signs, symptoms, risk factors
Usually inexpensive	Generally involves additional costs
Usually undertaken first	Usually undertaken as a follow-up to passive monitoring but may be the first line approach where there is a significant ULD risk.
Data coding and analysis is usually simple	In depth data coding and analysis require specialist assistance.
Non-clinical	Non-clinical and clinical indicators included
Readily established as information sources usually designed for other administrative purposes.	Recommended when faced with an 'outbreak' of ULDs

125 Some initial value can be gained from passive monitoring but active monitoring builds on this information and enables an in-depth look at risk factors, signs and symptoms in a specific workplace. Consultation with employees is particularly important since there are ethical considerations relating to the handling of personal health information.

Examples of passive and active monitoring

Some examples of passive and active monitoring methods are given in Table 2.

Table 2 **Passive and active monitoring methods**

Passive	Active
Accident book/First aid record Compensation data	Workplace walkthroughs Body mapping
Statutory reporting systems (RIDDOR)[38]	Task analysis
Medical retirement reports	Confidential questionnaires
Symptoms reported	Health interviews
Sickness absence records	Health examinations
Production productivity and quality measures	Exposure checklist[27]
Staff turnover	
Health and safety meetings	
Morale and employee satisfaction	

Monitoring outcomes

126 In interpreting information obtained from monitoring it is useful to look for consistent patterns in:

- comments from employees;
- symptoms reported;
- existing risk factors;
- results of surveys.

127 Comparisons between groups of employees in different locations within the organisation may be helpful particularly where similar work is being undertaken. Where practicable, comparing your experiences with other companies in your sector may also assist in evaluating the performance of your control measures.[42, 43]

128 Where problems are identified, action should be taken to revise the measures in your management policy to improve control of the risk. Employees should be advised of the situation and any appropriate medical management made available. Further monitoring will determine if these revised measures have been effective.

Reviewing

129 Reviewing provides an opportunity to look at the overall performance of your systems for managing ULD risks and should be considered as an integral part of the management process. It should be undertaken when monitoring suggests that the current policy/programme is not adequately controlling the risks or when technical developments or organisational changes are planned which may alter the levels of risk.

130 Reviewing relies largely on the use of existing management information and may often be incorporated in a periodic review of business effectiveness, eg, as part of a quality programme.

131 Reviewing:

- needs to be systematic in approach;
- makes full use of existing management resources;
- is an opportunity to learn from experiences gained in managing ULD risk factors, signs and symptoms;
- determines whether interventions continue to be effective;
- establishes whether risks have been controlled where reasonably practicable;
- provides an opportunity to assess whether improved control measures should be introduced.

132 A system should be in place to ensure that the outcomes from the review are acted upon, feeding back into the management system as shown in Figure 1.

Appendices

47

Appendix 1:   **Case studies**

These case studies have been divided into the stages presented in the management model shown in Figure 1. This has been done retrospectively so all stages of the model are not always fully represented.

Case study A: Easter egg and chocolate box packing

Background

1   A large factory identified a number of tasks that created a risk of ULDs:

- **Task 1: Easter egg packing** For packing Easter eggs, eight separate components were assembled by hand. Most of these components arrived as flat-packs which then had to be folded and bent into the correct shape. The operators on this task were paid piecework rates dependent upon the number of eggs they assembled in a workday.
- **Task 2: Chocolate box packing** During the production of boxes of chocolates, two layers of chocolates in a plastic moulded tray, a pad of corrugated cardboard, and the 'unit key' (ie to identify the filling in the chocolate) were needed to be packed into different-size boxes. The boxes were presented to the operator on a moving conveyor, and, as they went past, different operators had to put different components (the chocolates, the mouldings in which they sit, the cardboard pad, and information leaflets) into the boxes in a flow assembly operation.

Understand the issues and commit to action

2   The company physiotherapist and other medical department staff were seeing people from the egg and chocolate packaging department with ULDs. With the permission of the employees concerned, management had become aware of ULD referrals and had directed action on the issue.

Create the right organisational environment

3   The company doctor, the operations manager and the industrial engineer for the site

worked with employees throughout the process of assessment. Trials of solutions to reduce the risks were also done in a participative manner.

Assess the risk of ULDs in your workplace

4   A risk assessment of task, environment and individual factors for ULDs identified the following risk factors:

Task 1: Easter egg packing	
Task-related factors	
Repetition:	This task was highly repetitive with workers performing the same finger, wrist, arm and shoulder movements many times per minute.
Working posture:	The task required many movements of the hand and wrist, eg sideways bending and bending the wrists up and down while folding the cardboard and snapping a plastic cover over the eggs. The elbow was often held and moved in positions away from the body.
Force:	Snapping of the plastic cover over the eggs required force with pinch grip.
Duration of exposure:	Workers conducted this task for prolonged periods each day.
Environment-related factors	
Psychosocial factors:	Workers were paid on a piecework basis which may have encouraged them to push themselves beyond the point at which they experienced discomfort. This may also have influenced the workers' willingness to report upper limb discomfort for fear of reduced working hours/speed etc.

Task 2: Chocolate box packing	
Task-related factors	
Repetition:	This task was highly repetitive with workers performing the same upper limb movements many times per minute. The operator's work rate was determined by the conveyor speed.
Working posture:	The box design made it difficult to place the components accurately in the boxes when the conveyor was moving quickly. This meant that workers assumed awkward postures of the shoulder and wrist.
Duration of exposure:	Workers undertook this task for prolonged periods each day.

5   If workers were rotating between the two tasks, they may have been at an increased risk of ULDs. Both tasks present very similar risk factors for ULDs (repetition of similar upper limb postures for long periods) and in combination, further increase the risk of ULDs. This example highlights the importance of looking at the risk assessments of tasks in combination where workers are performing multiple tasks during the shift.

Reduce the risk of ULDs

6   After the assessment was completed it was determined that certain elements needed to be redesigned:

- the packing operation was redesigned to remove the risk element of cardboard bending and the snapping shut of the plastic mould. This reduced the number of uncomfortable wrist and hand movements;
- the pay structure was changed from piecework to salaried work;
- for chocolate box assembly, engineers developed a mock-up workstation to trial with operators in which the rate of completion of the task was determined by the operator, not by the conveyor;
- a single operator undertook the whole assembly task rather than putting one component in the box (ie job enlargement);
- engineers worked out the best angle for viewing the components, for taking them off the conveyor, and for assembling them without twisting and turning;
- after testing out this design with the participation of the operators the new line was built and installed.

Manage any episodes of ULDs

7   The company employs a physiotherapist and other medical department staff in order to manage any episodes of ULDs and facilitate rehabilitation and return to work where possible.

Carry out regular checks on programme effectiveness

8   For Easter egg packing:

- fewer cases of wrist and hand problems are now reported to medical staff;
- overall efficiency of the production line has improved;
- the number of units damaged has decreased, and the visual quality of the finished product has improved;
- the amount of material (chocolate, plastic, cardboard) wasted has decreased;
- staff morale has improved;
- the egg production workflow is easier to manage and regulate; and
- there needs to be less staff rotation because the nature of the job has improved.

9   For the chocolate box packing:

- operator comfort has increased, as the adjustability in each workstation can be used to meet each operator's needs;
- assembly quality has improved, as the operators are no longer trying to put the components into a moving box.

10   Packing operations are performed manually in a range of different industries. As this case study illustrates, the operator is often required to use positions of the hand and wrist, which can lead to upper limb disorders, especially when combined with high force and/or repetition. The company has benefited in both production efficiency and staff well being and health by recognising risks within the task, and investing in ergonomic changes to the tasks and packaging materials.

Case study B: Computer use in news media organisation

The work covered by this case study was subject to the Display Screen Equipment Regulations. This case study shows how the structured approach in the guidance can help comply with the Regulations in an unusual situation with complex challenges.

Background

11   For many years a large news media organisation had used a computer-based system to store and transfer news stories. This was gradually becoming outdated and required upgrading due to developments in the electronic transfer of stories and the need for a faster more efficient system.

12   A new 'off-the-shelf' package based on an existing and widely used system was chosen. Some adaptations were made for the current organisation and it was installed in the newsroom and elsewhere. Accompanying the rollout was a programme of change management that included advice on implementation, installation and training for users including workstation adjustment and posture.

Understand the issues and commit to action

13   The use of the new system led to unanticipated consequences because it was being used for a task for which it was not designed – the preparation of sometimes lengthy, in-depth news stories rather than short bulletin-style pieces.

14   Prior to the introduction of the new system, comparatively few cases of ULDs had arisen even though computerised technology had been in use for many years. There then followed a rapid surge in new cases in the order of a three to four fold increase over the previous years.

Create the right organisational environment

15   Right from the beginning an open-minded policy was adopted so that all staff could be kept fully informed of the extent of the problem and its progress.

Assess the risk of ULDs in your workplace

16   Assessment of task, environment and individual factors for ULDs revealed that the software did not cope with page breaks, spell checking, cut-and-paste editing facilities and the need for the news organisation to cope with non-English material. The task of text input and editing against constant deadlines was now much more onerous than with a standard word processing style package. Unfortunately the implementation of this new system coincided with the outbreak of a major international news event necessitating an enormous increase in workload. In addition, organisational changes were being made to

the business infrastructure in common with those being made elsewhere at the time. This inevitably led to uncertainty about the future, insecurity on the part of the workforce, and to higher levels of stress.

17   Identified risk factors for ULDs included:

Task-related factors	
Repetition:	Staff were performing multiple mouse clicks as well as highly repetitive keying.
Working posture:	Position of the keyboard, mouse and monitor meant that static contraction of the shoulder and neck muscles was occurring when workers were using the input devices and/or looking at the screen. Wrist postures were also problematic for some workers.
Duration of exposure:	Text input and editing tasks were performed for prolonged periods each day. The outbreak of the major ongoing news event meant that many workers were working longer hours.
Environment-related factors	
Psychosocial factors:	Organisational changes, strict deadlines and workload associated with the major news event were all identified as psychosocial risk factors.

Reduce the risk of ULDs

18   Controls to reduce the risk of ULDs were implemented as follows:

- computer related equipment which included hardware, software and furniture was reviewed by the safety manager;
- changes to workstation layout were made to improve working postures, particularly in relation to the upper limb and mouse and keyboard use. This focused on the risk factor of working posture;
- changes were made to the software to reduce repetition;
- the manager altered the work organisation including work patterns and shifts. This rectified any adverse work practices and included control over work quality and deadlines. These controls focused on the risk factors of duration and psychosocial factors.

Manage any episodes of ULDs

19   Early reporting of individual cases to the occupational health department was encouraged so that steps could be taken by managers to minimise the impact of symptoms. Three main routes of management were drawn up:

- a self-help route including a range of physical therapies and relaxation exercises;
- a therapeutic route to investigate symptoms and signs, carry out diagnostic and other investigations and refer, as appropriate, for treatment options – done by the occupational health department. Treatment could include medication, onward referral to GP or specialist, physiotherapy or counselling;
- from initial onset or reporting of symptoms, a cycle of four weeks was allowed for the above to be accomplished, after which a case conference/review meeting would take place to determine if the individual was now fit and could return to work, was improving and could return to modified work or where the programme had failed and a job change was required.

Carry out regular checks on programme effectiveness

20   After several years from the initial outbreak the number of original cases had halved, of which more than 60% were deemed to be cured or dormant.

21   This study shows that the outlook for the majority of cases should be good so long as a programme is adopted which encourages early reporting and management of cases without fear of prejudice, in an environment of mutual co-operation between employees, managers, unions, safety officers, IT specialists and occupational health professionals.

Case Study C: Healthcare product packing

Background

22   A large manufacturing company with several factory sites produces and packs a wide range of cosmetic and skin care products. These often have short packing run times, and some product lines are difficult to automate. The company recognised that the highly manual packaging tasks presented a risk of ULDs and took measures to tackle these.

Understanding the issues and commit to action

23 The company identified the need to take action to reduce the risk of ULDs and for a proactive system to manage ULD referrals/cases across the different factory sites. This was met through the development of a company ULD policy. A company ergonomist was also recruited to develop and facilitate an ergonomics programme.

Create the right organisational environment

24 Managers and operators had been aware of reported symptoms of ULDs and were supportive of measures to reduce these. From the start the ergonomist worked closely with occupational health staff and management.

25 Packing team leaders and senior team members with responsibility for the health and safety of their particular area were trained in safety risk assessment and the identification of possible risk reduction measures.

Assess the risk of ULDs in the workplace

26 A three-stage risk assessment process was set up:

- detailed risk assessments of the packaging tasks were undertaken using the rapid upper limb assessment (RULA) method[28] and a body part discomfort and psychosocial survey. These formed the basis for prioritising risk reduction recommendations;
- senior team members regularly assess the risk of ULDs during routine risk assessments of their packing lines. They are encouraged to identify and implement risk reduction measures and can seek advice from the company ergonomist;
- when a new product is to be introduced to a line, a 'change control assessment' is undertaken to identify any specific problems which may relate to the packing of that product, and possible solutions.

An example of a task identified during a packing trial risk assessment as posing a ULD risk was sealing a two-piece glass jar using a wire metal clasp. The task required repetitive activity and the application of force to close the clasp. There was also the risk of pressure points on the palm from the wire.

The risk of ULDs associated with the task was reduced by encouraging operators to stand rather than sit to make it easier to apply force; providing a leather palm protector; ensuring two people undertook the task to reduce duration of exposure and increase recovery time; and providing guidance on task procedure. After implementation, no ULD symptoms were reported from this packing operation.

Reduce the risk of ULDs

27   The following measures apply to all packing lines:

- all packing employees rotate to a different task every 30 minutes. Where possible, rotated tasks are significantly different in terms of upper limb movements required;
- increased automation, standardisation of packaging, and ways of reducing repetitive movements are sought at the design stage (eg reducing the number of turns required to fasten a lid);
- development of procedures that encourage operators to adopt good postures and movements on packing tasks;
- the development and availability of risk reducing aids (eg tools and equipment);
- increased awareness of ULD issues among the workforce, and encouragement of all employees to participate in identifying risk reduction measures and solutions.

Educate and inform your workforce

28   A leaflet on ULDs, covering causes of ULDs, how to identify signs and symptoms, and what to do if these are experienced, was issued to all staff with a follow-up issue after 18 months.

29   Where appropriate, awareness training is provided by the company ergonomist to promote suitable working techniques that can be used to reduce ULD risk.

Manage any episodes of ULDs

30   The company policy requires employees to report any ULD symptoms to their team leader who refers them to the occupational health service. Their workstation and tasks are

assessed in light of the problems experienced and appropriate recommendations given. The team leader reviews the situation weekly, and occupational health staff regularly monitor the employee's symptoms.

Carry out regular checks on programme effectiveness

31   Regular health and safety group meetings (involving senior management, occupational health staff, the company ergonomist, factory engineers and safety representatives) review risk management issues and the impact of risk reduction measures taken. They also provide effective routes of communication between staff involved.

32   Following the initial awareness raising campaign (which included issue of the ULD leaflet) there was an expected increase in referrals to the occupational health service. This was followed by a steady reduction in referral rate over the following two years. When the leaflet was re-issued the anticipated increase in referrals was not experienced.

33   There are ongoing reviews of occupational health data, and a follow-up body part discomfort survey is planned to evaluate the impact of the risk reduction programme.

Case Study D: New counter design for cashiers

Background

34   A leading bookmaker's group with over 11 000 staff and 2 000 shops planned to roll-out a radically new design of electronic point-of-sales (EPOS) system and associated counter. Prevention of ULD risks was a major consideration in the selection of equipment, design of the counter, furniture and software. The new design and management programme had to accommodate a range of shop environments, staff regularly moving between premises and different cashier workstations.

35   The cashier's task for which the new design was specified mainly involves sitting at the workstation and dealing with transactions (handling betting slips and money). The EPOS system involves some computer work (keyboard and mouse use) to handle and process bets.

Understand the issues and commit to action

36   Management recognised that ULD risk factors were present in the cashier's task eg

repetitively reaching to the counter top and awkward stretches to reach equipment. Senior management was supportive of the plan to introduce new counter design guidelines and recognised the potential impact on occupational health.

Create the right organisational environment

37 It was agreed that the new counter design and layout should be based on ergonomics criteria. Management also recognised that providing information to employees and having a means of identifying any health problems was essential in managing occupational health. A project team was assembled with representatives from facilities management, health and safety, IT and IT development, line management, and the general workforce to specify and develop the new counter layout and associated equipment.

Assess the risk of ULDs in the workplace

38 A risk assessment identified that certain movements and tasks would be required (reaching to counter top, cash drawer, handling money etc) which contained the ULD risk factors of repetition, reaching and awkward posture. This enabled ergonomics criteria to be specified for the counter design.

Reduce the risk of ULDs

39 To reduce the risks of ULDs:

- ergonomics advice was sought for body dimension criteria on which to base the counter design;
- mock-ups of counters were trialled by cashiers;
- computer related equipment including scanner, printer and screen, and their layout were reviewed and trialled to reduce the risk of ULDs and ensure their ease of use, (eg scanning rather than keyboard use was selected for data entry and equipment was placed within the zone of comfortable reach);
- the software design reduced the pressure on cashiers by helping with management of deadlines, for example, taking bets in relation to when races started;
- management also ensured that there were sufficient staff in each shop to allow rest and recovery during the shift, and to cover particularly busy periods.

Educate and inform your workforce

40   Information on setting up the workstation and chair adjustment was provided on the company intranet to which all cashiers have access. In addition, on an ongoing basis employees are prompted to complete an on-line assessment of their workstation after a certain number of log-ons. This also directs staff to relevant guidance documentation.

Manage any episodes of ULDs

41   Most health problems are identified in the on-line assessment or through the absence management system. Any problems identified are reported to the employee's line manager, and to the safety manager, and it is the line manager's responsibility to action change (eg replace faulty equipment). Where a problem has been identified the employee completes an on-line assessment 21 days after the initial report. If the problem has not been resolved it is reported to a higher level of manager, and a re-assessment is completed after a further 21 days. Continuing problems are reported to a director of the company. This provides an incentive for reported problems to be dealt with rapidly and ensures that awareness is raised among all staff.

42   Expert medical and ergonomics support is available for any employee with an ongoing health problem, so that individual workstations can be assessed and appropriate adjustments made.

Carry out regular checks on programme effectiveness

43   An expert ergonomic evaluation of the new counters identified that they did not pose a significant risk of ULDs. Ongoing monitoring of occupational health data continues. Further investigation is taking place into the design of betting slips to allow more electronic recognition of options (ie using tick boxes) so that the amount of mouse use by cashiers dealing with transactions can be reduced.

Case Study E: Addressing ULDs in poultry processing

Background

44   A large poultry processing company with a number of different sites wanted to systematically tackle their ULD problems.

Understand the issues and commit to action

45   The company had received guidance from their industry federation and was aware of the extent of ULD problems in the sector. There had also been a significant number of referrals to their occupational health department and claims for ULDs, which acted as a motivator to tackle these issues. Although managers had been aware of the issues, attitudes changed significantly when the cost of placing people with ULDs onto lighter duties was calculated, and found to be considerable.

Create the right organisational environment

46   Following a review of their health and safety management systems, the company established a programme for the prevention of ULDs. Policies were written, arrangements and procedures put in place, and roles and responsibilities clarified.

47   Multidisciplinary ergonomics teams were created, involving all levels of the business and led by line managers. Teams were given an ergonomics training programme to raise awareness of the issues and identify ways of reducing the risks. In addition, the company's occupational health nurses were given a more proactive role in managing ULDs and worked closely with first line managers.

Assess the risk of ULDs in the workplace

48   The ULD risk assessments were integrated into the safety management of the business. General risk assessments are done by trained risk assessors under the guidance of the line manager of the department. The assessment considers a range of risks and uses specific checklists for ULDs, manual handling and ergonomics issues. If these identify a potential ULD risk, a person trained in ergonomics or an occupational health nurse undertakes a more detailed assessment.

Reduce the risk of ULDs

49   Because staff on the shop floor have had ergonomics training they have been able to generate many workplace improvements themselves. It is primarily through the empowerment and commitment of the first line managers that the process has been successful.

'Chicken hang on'

One of the poultry processing activities involves hanging chilled whole birds onto moving shackle lines so that they can be cut into chicken portions by a machine. The task requires individual birds to be picked from a hopper situated in front of the operator and the legs of the bird placed in the shackle on a suspended conveyor. The operators carrying out this task work in teams of three, at a rate of 70 birds per minute. A decision was taken to replace the cut up machines and, as a part of that project, to redesign the 'hang-on' workstation to reduce the ULD risk and the wasteful handling involved in the existing process.

A detailed assessment revealed the following:

Task related risk factors	
Repetition:	The task was highly repetitive with up to 25 cycles per minute. The task was also machine paced.
Working postures:	Workers had to reach forward and down to pick up the birds, then up to place them in the shackle. Positioning the bird to align with the shackle also required awkward postures.
Force:	Some force was required to place birds in the shackle; Birds weigh up to 2 kgs.
Duration of exposure:	Workers conducted this task for prolonged periods each day.
Environment related risk factors	
Working environment:	Low workroom temperature (12 °C) and low temperature of product (3 °C)
Psychosocial factors:	The work was machine paced.

A two-phase re-design was implemented to reduce, and ultimately eliminate, the risk.

Phase 1
Redesigned workstation – reduced height of shackle on conveyor; repositioned bird delivery hopper so the reach distances required were reduced; redesigned shackle to make attachment easier. Employees were consulted and involved in the design of the revised workplace.

Phase 2
Direct feed of birds from another shackle line, to the shackle line on the automatic cut up machine, thus eliminating the need to manually hang birds.

Outcomes include:
Significant reduction in ergonomic risk; reduction of reported ULDs from the activity; reduction in number of employees on lighter duties from this operation; a marked improvement in productivity.

Educate and inform your workforce

50   All staff receive induction training which covers the risk of ULDs, control measures and reporting procedures. Further information and training are given on the job. The profile of ULDs has been raised within the company and there is open communication about the issue.

Manage any episodes of ULDs

51   If an employee experiences ULD symptoms they are referred through their line manager to the occupational health department who will assess their condition and work, and make recommendations concerning appropriate action (workplace or task modifications, rest, lighter duties). Occupational health staff undertake on-going surveillance of those with problems. A physiotherapist is available on site to treat and advise those with ULDs.

Carry out regular checks on programme effectiveness

52   The company undertakes a six monthly audit of the ULD programme to review the management system and procedures, their effectiveness and the impact they have had, and to identify any further improvements.

53   Recent examination of the cost of placing people on light duties (largely due to ULDs) identified that in a sample week in 1998 of 2300 processing staff, 60 (2.6%) were on light duties. Following the ergonomics programme, in the same sample week in 2001 only 16 staff (0.7%) were on light duties. In direct labour costs alone the company estimate that this reduction equates to a saving of £500 000. In one factory, the number of people placed on light duties has fallen by almost 80% in this period.

Appendix 2: **Risk Filter and Risk Assessment Worksheets**

The aim of the Risk Filter is to set out an approximate threshold below which the risk of ULDs is likely to be low. The guidelines in the Risk Filter and Worksheets are provided as an aid to risk assessment. They have been developed from the scientific literature and from expert opinion. As such, they are not precise exposure limits, but are intended to help you to identify the potential risks and possible measures to reduce them.

Other methods of assessment are available and may be equally appropriate in assessing the level of risk of ULDs. [27,28,29,30]

Overview

1   Together the Risk Filter and Risk Assessment Worksheets provide a two-stage assessment process, which may be photocopied for use:

- Stage one: Use the Risk Filter to help identify situations where a more detailed assessment is necessary. (Please note that certain risk factors have been purposely omitted in the filter in order to provide a useable, first stage, screening tool.)
- Stage two: Use the Risk Assessment Worksheets to conduct a more detailed risk assessment for those tasks identified by the Risk Filter

2   Before undertaking your assessment, you should read 'Assess the risk of ULDs in your workplace' (which provides guidance on risk assessment and risk factors) (see paragraphs 43-86). In order for your assessment to be effective you should:

- involve your workforce in the assessment and control process to take advantage of their intimate knowledge of the work;
- explain to the worker(s) what you are doing prior to assessing a task. You should always emphasise that the assessment is of the task and not the worker's performance;
- walk through the area and identify any tasks that relate to display screen equipment or involve manual handling because you also need to refer to specific guidance on the relevant regulations to assess these;
- make sure that you have spent some time observing the job and what you are seeing is representative of normal working procedures;
- observe all the workers for a short period of time where several people do the same job, to ensure that you have some insight into the demands of the job from all workers' perspectives;

- complete the assessment in the workplace (where possible, and if it is safe to do so);
- focus on the upper limb at each step ensuring you consider the fingers, hands, arms, elbows, shoulders and neck;
- where the Risk Filter indicates further action move on to stage two of the assessment using the Risk Assessment Worksheets.

3   Equipment that may be useful includes:

- stopwatch or timer to measure cycle times;
- video camera to allow for more detailed analysis of movement cycles, and for the assessment to be finalised away from the workplace if necessary;
- scales/force guage (spring balance and string) to measure the weight/forces related to upper limb activities.

Read the following guidance in conjunction with the risk filter.

Duration:

A consideration of duration, or exposure time, as a risk factor for ULDs would include both the length of time that a task is performed in a typical working day as well as how often it is repeated (eg daily, weekly or less often). Building such a complex factor into a simple risk filter and worksheet is difficult. '2 consecutive hours' or 'more than 2 hours total per workday' have been used as basic building blocks of exposure time throughout the guidelines in the risk filter and risk assessment worksheets. 'Consecutive' in this context means the task or similar groups of tasks are repeated successively throughout the 2 hour period. It must be emphasised that the 2 hour period is not a limit and should be applied pragmatically.

For example, if a task was performed for 1 hour and 40 minutes, followed by a 10 minute break, then for another 1 hour and 40 minutes, followed by another break, and so on, throughout an 8 hour workday, the worker has not strictly worked more than '2 consecutive hours'. The duration of exposure for this task, however, is certainly high and would be of concern if the other risk factors for ULD were also present. Conversely, if the task requirements are exceptionally demanding, a duration of less than '2 consecutive hours' may present an unacceptable risk.

STAGE 1: Risk Filter procedure

Ensure you have read 'Assess the risk of ULDs in your workplace' and the general guidance at the beginning of this Appendix prior to undertaking your assessment.

4   Completing the Filter involves:

- recording the basic details of the task such as the date, name of the task, the assessor and task description;
- probably using a separate Filter sheet for each task;
- going through each step in turn and placing a tick in each box where you observe examples of these risks;
- planning a more detailed risk assessment if any of the risk factors are ticked;
- identifying those tasks with the most risk factors (the more there are the greater the risk) to help in prioritising tasks for the second stage risk assessment.

5   **Step 1: Signs and symptoms:** Look for:

- actual cases of ULDs in work:
    - review sickness absence records and medical certificates received;
    - ask your occupational health service for anonymous information about cases of ULDs;
- complaints of aches or pains:
    - check the accident book and or treatment book for mention of 'sprains and strains' and any other types of aches and pains;
    - talk to managers, supervisors and workers;
- improvised changes to work equipment, furniture or tools:
    - walk through the workplace to identify improvised changes;
    - check with managers, supervisors and workers for "difficult" jobs or those which have become more "difficult" recently.

6   **Step 2: Repetition:** Check for frequent movements for prolonged periods. Examples may include repeated hand press operations, repeated triggering operations, repeated cutting actions, repeated handling etc.

A 'Cycle' refers to a sequence of actions of relatively short duration that is repeated over and over, and is almost always the same. They are not necessarily associated with one single joint movement, (such as the elbow), but with movements of one or more parts of the limb (such as reaching, manipulating and placing an object). Cycles are not always clear-cut, and in such cases observers should look for similar actions that are repeated.

A simple task may consist of a sequence of movements which would be repeated and therefore form the cycle. A more complex task may consist of elements (as described in paragraph 53) some or all of which may be distinct cycles.

65

7   **Step 3: Working postures:** Check for postures that are awkward and/or held for prolonged periods in a static or fixed position. Check fingers, wrists, hands, arms, shoulders and necks. Remember: The more the joints deviate from their neutral position, the greater the risk.

8   **Step 4: Force:** Check for sustained or repeated application of force.

9   **Step 5: Vibration:** Make a note of the type of vibrating tools or equipment such as grinders, polishers etc. that are used for the stage 2 assessment.

You should also be aware that psychosocial and working environment factors (such as high job demands and lack of control, cold and lighting) could further increase the risk of ULDs. These factors are expanded in the full risk assessment.

RISK FILTER

Task: _____

Assessor: _____

Date: _____ **Location/work area:** _____

IF YOU ANSWER YES TO ANY OF THE STEPS, YOU SHOULD THEN MAKE A FULL RISK ASSESSMENT OF THE TASK. REMEMBER TO CONSIDER EACH OF THE BODY PARTS OF THE UPPER LIMBS (FINGERS, HANDS, WRISTS, ARMS, SHOULDERS AND NECK). ANSWER **ALL** QUESTIONS

Step 1: Signs and symptoms

Are there any:	Are any of these present?		
☐ Medically diagnosed cases of ULDs in this work?		YES ☐	Move on to Step 2
☐ Complaints of aches or pains?			
☐ Improvised changes to work equipment, furniture or tools?		NO ☐	

Step 2: Repetition

Are there any repetitive elements such as:	For more than 2 hours total per shift?		
☐ Repeating the same motions every few seconds?		YES ☐	Move on to Step 3
☐ A sequence of movements repeated more than twice per minute?			
☐ More than 50% of the cycle time involved in performing the same sequence of motions?		NO ☐	

Step 3: Working postures

Are there any working postures such as:	For more than 2 hours total per shift?		
☐ Large range of joint movement such as side to side or up and down?		YES ☐	Move on to Step 4
☐ Awkward or extreme joint positions?			
☐ Joints held in fixed positions?		NO ☐	
☐ Stretching to reach items or controls?			
☐ Twisting or rotating items or controls?			
☐ Working overhead?			

Step 4: Force

Are there any forces applied such as:	Sustained or repeated application of force for more than 2 hours total per shift ?		
☐ Pushing, pulling, moving things (including with the fingers or thumb)?		YES ☐	Move on to Step 5
☐ Grasping/gripping?			
☐ Pinch grips ie holding or grasping objects between thumb and finger?		NO ☐	
☐ Steadying or supporting items or work pieces?			
☐ Shock and/or impact being transmitted to the body from tools or equipment?			
☐ Objects creating localised pressure on any part of the upper limb?			

Step 5: Vibration

	Regularly (ie. at some point during most shifts)?	
☐ Do workers use any powered hand-held or hand-guided tools or equipment or do they hand-feed work pieces to vibrating equipment?		YES ☐
		NO ☐

If you answer yes to any of the steps, you should make a full risk assessment of the task.

67

STAGE 2: Risk Assessment Worksheets procedure

Read the following guidance in conjunction with the Risk Assessment Sheets overleaf. Ensure you have read 'Assess the risks of ULDs in your workplace' (see paragraphs 43-86) and the general guidance at the beginning of this Appendix prior to undertaking your assessment.

n.b. The risk factor of 'duration' is addressed within the guidance values for other risk factors and therefore does not have a heading in its own right.

10   Completing the Risk Assessment Worksheets involves:

- using a set of Worksheets for each task;
- recording basic task details on the Worksheets, such as how long the task is carried out, a task description etc. (An example task description is: a worker reaches for screws, places them in position at head height, then uses counterbalanced drill to fix screws. The finished product is then pushed across the body to the next station);
- going through each risk factor in turn, observing the task(s) in relation to the appropriate guidelines to see if a risk of ULDs is present;
- recording which aspects of the task(s) present the risk;
- noting down possible control options;
- identifying those tasks with the most risk factors to help in prioritising tasks for a programme of control (the more 'yes' ticks the greater the risk).

Completing each risk factor

11   The following procedures should be observed when completing each risk factor:

- place a tick in the 'Yes' box where you observe examples of these risk factors and a tick in the 'No' box when you do not;
- write down what the person is doing in relation to that risk factor in the next column, including:
    - body part affected;
    - how long the task is being done, for example number of times per minute, number of hours per day. (eg five times per minute, five shifts of 7.5 hours);
    - what aspects of the task are presenting the risk;
    - type of work equipment;
    - whether any reference numerical values are exceeded (possibly indicating an elevated level of risk for ULDs)

■ write down any possible control measures that can be taken to minimise the risk of injury in the second last column. Some control options are listed in the final column, these are explained in further detail in Appendix 2: 'Suggestions for reducing the risk'. The controls listed represent some options only and are not an exhaustive list.

Completing the action plan

12 The following procedures should be observed when completing the action plan:

■ summarise and prioritise the control options;
- examine the completed risk assessment and the identified control options to prioritise action. Identify tasks with the highest number of 'Yes' ticks. Tasks with a higher number of 'Yes' ticks may require more immediate action;
- where you have established that there are diagnosed cases of ULDs or complaints of discomfort etc. as well as risk factors, view this combination as a high priority for implementing control measures
■ develop a short, medium and long term strategy to implement controls, and place dates against these;
■ enter a date for re-evaluation in the action plan table to ensure that implementation dates are monitored.

RISK ASSESSEMENT WORKSHEETS

Date: _____

Name of assessor: _____

Task: _____

No. of employees that conduct this task _____

How long is the task typically undertaken for:

a)   without a break: _____

b)   in a typical shift (excluding breaks): _____

_____

How frequently is the task undertaken
(eg. daily, weekly): _____

Other tasks undertaken by worker that may
pose risk of ULDs *(include worksheet reference numbers)*:

_____

What hand tools are used in the task: _____

_____

_____

I Repetition		Yes	No	**Describe any problem(s) and probable cause(s):** *Describe what the person is doing eg. hand operation of drill 10 times per minute. Performed 3 hours per day, five days per week.*
For 2 consecutive hours per work day:				
1.1 Does the task involve repeating the same movements every few seconds?	A '**Cycle**' is a sequence of actions of relatively short duration that is repeated over and over, and is almost always the same. A cycle is not necessarily associated with one single joint movement, but also with complex movements of one or more parts of the body.	☐	☐	
1.2 Is there a cycle or sequence of movements that is repeated twice per minute or more **OR** More than 50% of the task involves performing a repetitive sequence of motions?		☐	☐	
1.3 Are the wrists/hands/fingers used intensively?		☐	☐	
1.4 Is there repetitive shoulder/arm movement (ie regular arm movement with some pauses or almost continuous arm movement?)		☐	☐	
1.5 Are tools used that require **repetitive** finger or thumb action?		☐	☐	

Worksheet Reference Number	

Task description:

	Describe any risk control options you have identified	**Control options** *(not exhaustive list)*
		Reduce repetition: ■ Mechanise or automate repetitive functions ■ Use power/ratchet tools ■ Remove machine or other pacing ■ Restructure task (Job design) ■ Remove or monitor piecework schemes **Reduce duration:** ■ Implement job enlargement ■ Ensure adequate breaks ■ Implement job rotation ■ Limit / control overtime

2 **Working posture** **Fingers, hands and wrist**		Yes	No	**Describe any problem(s) and probable cause(s):** *Note problem postures and identify parts of the upper limb involved. eg. Static gripping posture used for up to 2 hours at a time, wrists repetitively bent sideways when drilling objects.*
2.1 Is the wrist bent **repetitively** up and/or down?	*Remember: the greater the deviation from a neutral position, the greater the risk.*	☐	☐	
2.2 Is the wrist **held** in a position that is bent upwards or downwards?		☐	☐	
2.3 Are the fingers gripping or used while the wrists are bent?		☐	☐	
2.4 Is the wrist bent **repetitively** to either side?		☐	☐	
2.5 Is the wrist **held** bent to either side?		☐	☐	
2.6 Are the hands **repetitively** turned or twisted so that the palm is facing up or downwards?		☐	☐	
2.7 Are the hands **held** with the palms facing up or down?		☐	☐	
2.8 Is a wide finger and/or hand span needed to grip, hold or manipulate items?		☐	☐	
2.9 Do static postures of the fingers, hand or wrist occur, for more than two consecutive hours per work day?		☐	☐	
2.10 Are there tools, equipment and/or work pieces that are poorly shaped and/or do not fit the hand comfortably?		☐	☐	
2.11 Are there any tools, hand held equipment or work pieces that are too large or small to be gripped easily?		☐	☐	
2.12 Are tools designed for right handed use only?		☐	☐	

	Describe any risk control options you have identified	Control options *(not exhaustive list)*
		Optimise working posture: ■ Modify operation or production method ■ Relocate equipment or items ■ Present work items differently ■ Reduce amount of manipulation required ■ Ensure equipment accounts for differences in worker size, shape and strength ■ Ensure working heights are appropriate ■ Ensure items are within reach distances ■ Provide suitable (and adjustable) seating ■ Use fixtures/jigs ■ Alter tools or controls ■ Ensure tools are suitable for task ■ Ensure tools do not require awkward postures

3   Working posture

Arms and shoulders

		Yes	No

Describe any problem(s) and probable cause(s): *Note problem postures and identify parts of the upper limb involved. eg. Shoulder held in fixed position with elbow out to the side for up to 2 hours at a time. This is due to the work height.*

		Yes	No
3.1 Is work performed above the head or with the elbows above the shoulders for more than 2 hours total in a working day?	*Remember: the greater the deviation from a neutral position, the greater the risk.*	☐	☐
3.2 Does the task involve **repetitively** moving the upper arms out to the side of the body?		☐	☐
3.3 Does the task involve **holding** the upper arms out to the side of the body without support?		☐	☐
3.4 Do static postures of the shoulder or elbow occur, for more than two consecutive hours per work day?		☐	☐
3.5 Does the work involve any other postures such as: ☐ Awkward forward or sideways reaching? ☐ Awkward reaching behind the body? ☐ Awkward reaching across the body?	*Workstation layout and working height can be a major influence on working postures.*	☐	☐

4   Working posture

Head and neck

		Yes	No

Describe any problem(s) and probable cause(s): *Note problem postures and identify parts of the upper limb involved. eg. neck held in fixed bending position to see screw holes.*

		Yes	No
4.1 Does the task involve **repetitively** bending or twisting the neck?	*Remember: the greater the deviation from a neutral position, the greater the risk.*	☐	☐
4.2 Does the task involve **holding** the neck bent and/or twisted for more than 2 hours total per work day?		☐	☐
4.3 Do the visual demands of the task require the worker to view fine details and adopt awkward postures?		☐	☐
4.4 Do aspects of lighting such as dim light, shadow, flickering light, glare and/or reflections cause the worker to adopt awkward postures?		☐	☐

Describe any risk control options you have identified	Control options *(not exhaustive list)*
	Optimise working postures: ■ Automate or mechanise ■ Modify operation or production method ■ Relocate equipment or items ■ Present work items differently ■ Reduce amount of manipulation required ■ Ensure workplaces and equipment account for differences in worker size, shape and strength ■ Ensure working heights are appropriate ■ Ensure items are within reach distances ■ Provide suitable (and adjustable) seating ■ Use fixtures/jigs ■ Alter tools or controls ■ Ensure tools are suitable for task ■ Ensure tools do not require awkward postures ■ Provide arm support for precision work

Describe any risk control options you have identified	Control options *(not exhaustive list)*
	Optimise working postures: ■ Ensure visual requirements are not too demanding ■ Provide visual aids ■ Ensure lighting is suitable ■ Reposition items that workers are required to look at

5   Force

		Yes	No

Describe any problem(s) and probable cause(s): *eg. Drill handle is too small resulting in increased gripping force for up to 4 hours per day. Also high force applied to screws*

		Yes	No
5.1 Does the task require **repetitive** or **static** application of force?	*For the hand/wrist, high-force tasks are those with estimated average individual hand force requirements of 4 kg or above.*	☐	☐
5.2 Is a pinch grip being used **repetitively** or **statically** for more than two hours <u>total</u> per work day?	*For example, pinching an unsupported object weighing 0.9 kg (2 lbs) or more per hand, or using a similar pinching force (eg holding a small binder clip open).*	☐	☐
5.3 Does the worker use the tip of the finger, thumb or hand as a pressing tool?		☐	☐
5.4 Do tools require the application of pressure on a trigger or button?		☐	☐
5.5 Does the hand apply force by twisting objects/ tools or squeezing items?		☐	☐
5.6 Is the hand or wrist used as a hammer?		☐	☐
5.7 Is force being applied when the wrists are bent and/or with the arms raised?		☐	☐
5.8 Does the task require the wearing of gloves which affect gripping?		☐	☐
5.9 Do any objects, work pieces, tools or parts of the workstation impinge or create localised pressure on any part of the body?		☐	☐

Describe any risk control options you have identified	Control options
	(not exhaustive list)
	Reduce force: ■ Reduce forces necessary ■ Use power tools ■ Can the function be achieved differently? ■ Use jigs to hold items ■ Reduce weight of items ■ Present items differently ■ Increase mechanical advantage ■ Alter task to use stronger muscles ■ Use foot pedals ■ If gloves used check that they are appropriate ■ Maintain tools ■ Ensure tools are suitable for task ■ Improve handles ■ Use light weight tools ■ Use tool counterbalances ■ Ensure tool handles fit workers comfortably

6 Working environment		Yes	No	Describe any problem(s) and probable cause(s): *eg. Workers exposed to hand vibration from drill up to 4 hours per day. Workers have cold air blowing on hands from exhaust.*
6.1 Are vibration exposures likely to regularly exceed HSE's recommended action level of 2.8 m/s² A(8)? - Impulsive tools (chipping hammers, needle guns, hammer drills, etc.) may exceed HSE's recommended action level after only a few seconds use per day and are highly likely to exceed the action level after 30 minutes use per day - Rotary tools (grinders, sanders, etc.) may exceed HSE's recommended action level after only a few minutes use per day and are highly likely to exceed the action level after 2 hours use per day		☐	☐	
6. 2 Do tools create or transmit jerky actions, shock or torque (twisting)?		☐	☐	
6.3 Does the task involve working in cold or in draughts, particularly with cold air blowing over the hands?		☐	☐	
6.4 Does the task involve holding cold tool handles, work items or other cold objects?		☐	☐	

	Describe any risk control options you have identified	Control options *(not exhaustive list)*
		Improve the working environment: ■ Use alternative process(es) ■ Select alternative lower vibration equipment ■ Use balancers/ tensioners ■ Maintain equipment ■ Reduce exposure time to vibration ■ Provide information and training ■ Conduct health surveillance ■ Avoid working in cold ■ Avoid handling or insulate cold items or tools ■ Redirect blowing air ■ Use warm clothing

7 **Psychosocial factors** *(These factors are best dealt with through discussion with workers.* *Sensitivity may be required)*		Yes	No	**Describe any problem(s) and probable cause(s):** *eg. Workers are on piecework system.* *Support from supervision and co-workers is low.*
7.1 Is the work paced? ie machine or team sets the pace, or the work rate is otherwise not under the worker's control		☐	☐	
7.2 Is there a system of work, or piecework, which encourages workers to skip breaks or to finish early?		☐	☐	
7.3 Do workers find it difficult to keep up with their work?		☐	☐	
7.4 Do workers feel that there is a lack of support from supervisors or co-workers?		☐	☐	
7.5 Is there overtime/shiftwork that is unplanned, unmonitored and/or not organised to minimise risk of ULDs?		☐	☐	
7.6 Do the tasks require high levels of attention and concentration?		☐	☐	
7.7 Do the workers have little or no control over the way they do their work?		☐	☐	
7.8 Are there frequent tight deadlines to meet?		☐	☐	
7.9 Are there sudden changes in workload, or seasonal changes in volume without any mechanisms for dealing with the change?		☐	☐	
7.10 Do workers feel that they have been given sufficient training and information in order to carry out their job successfully?		☐	☐	

Describe any risk control options you have identified	Control options *(not exhaustive list)*
	Improve the working environment: ■ Reduce monotony ■ Ensure reasonable workload and deadlines ■ Ensure good communication and reporting of problems ■ Encourage teamwork ■ Monitor and control overtime and shiftwork ■ Reduce or monitor productivity relatedness of pay systems ■ Provide appropriate training

8 Individual differences	Yes	No	Describe any problem(s) and probable cause(s): *eg. No system for gradual return to work*
8.1 Are any workers potentially at increased risk of ULDs due to: ☐ being new employees or returning to work after a long break; ☐ differences in competence and skills; ☐ being part of vulnerable groups such as older, younger workers, new or expectant mothers; ☐ disability and health status.	☐	☐	

REMEMBER TO CONSIDER HOW THE RISK FACTORS INTERACT WITH EACH OTHER
(eg are forces applied repetitively in awkward posture etc)

ACTION PLAN

Worksheet reference	Controls to be implemented	Priority

	Describe any risk control options you have identified	Control options *(not exhaustive list)*
		■ Allow for a gradual build up to full production speed ■ Provide suitable training to develop the skills required ■ Seek advice on special requirements

Who is responsible for implementing controls?	Target implementation date	Date of re-evaluation

Suggestions for reducing the risk

*This is not an exhaustive list. Innovative ideas for controlling risks are often devised by workers or those familiar with the task.

Reducing repetition

Generally	Reduce the number of repetitive movements and the rate at which they are made, especially where these are combined with applying force and/or in awkward postures. Limit the duration of continuous work or restructure work methods to provide greater variety.
Automation and mechanisation	Can machinery do the highly repetitive functions and leave more varied jobs for the workers (Take care to avoid creating repetitive, boring and monotonous tasks to feed the machinery with work). Avoid pacing of the work. Automated machinery and team working can all act to increase the work rate. Aim to allow people to control their own pace of work.
Tools	Use power tools in place of manual tools. Use manual tools with ratchet devices to reduce the number of movements required, eg screwdrivers or spanners (see also 'Tools').
Job design	Break up long periods of frequent repetitions and static inactivity or spread repetitions across both hands. Share repetitive work through teamwork or job rotation. Distribute the workload over different muscle groups and joints.
Job enlargement	Consider adding extra activities to the job to provide variety in posture and speed of work.
Rest breaks	Breaks, before the onset of fatigue, are important. Consultation with workers may help to set an adequate work rest ratio or alternatively allocate times when workers should rotate from a specific task. Increase the frequency of breaks. Frequent short breaks are preferable to a few long ones.

Job rotation	Rotate the worker to perform other tasks, which varies body part action and speed. Remember that rotating to a task that utilises the same parts of the body and presents the same risk factors for injury as the original task will not provide rest periods for the parts of the body that are at risk of ULDs (see also 'Job rotation' in 'Reducing duration').
Overtime	Place a limit on or monitor overtime and provide sufficient rest breaks to account for prolonged exposure.

Optimising work postures

Poor workstation and equipment design is usually responsible for postural problems leading to ULDs. There are a number of methods for reducing postural problems.

Generally	Enable work to be done with the joints at about the mid points of their range of motion. Reduce the time spent holding and/or repeating awkward postures. Avoid using static postures for prolonged periods.
Workstation and tool design	Consider the location, angles and height of equipment, controls or work pieces in relation to the operator. Modify to improve posture. Ensure workplaces and work equipment are designed or selected to account for difference in size, shape and strength of workers. Alter tool design to improve wrist posture.
Work organisation and job design	Can changes be made 'upstream' of the job? ie does the task really have to be like this, or can alterations in the process elsewhere mean that items do not have to be assembled/presented in this way? Can the sequence be changed to make the task less awkward?
Presentation/ orientation of work items	Consider position of the work, and the use of fixtures and jigs to angle and hold work in more accessible positions. Consider how the body will interface with the equipment. Are there objects or attachments that act as obstacles and lead to poor posture?

Seating

Ensure seats are adjustable.

Ensure that there is sufficient space to enable workers to make effective use of the adjustable features of their chairs.

Do workers know how to adjust their chairs?

Ensure that there is sufficient leg space for the worker to stretch and make changes in leg and foot posture.

Confined leg space can constrain overall body posture.

Reach distances

Place equipment and materials within primary reach zones keeping repetitive reaching as close as possible to the body and always within 450 mm of the front of the operator. Figure 12 illustrates how the most frequently used items have been positioned within ease of reach areas of the worker.

Figure 12

For further information on reach distances, working zones and seating refer to *Seating at work*.[44]

Working height

Can the height, angle and position at which the work is being conducted be changed to improve visibility of the task?

Seated workstation tables should accommodate the largest users. Platforms, adjustable chairs and footrests can be used by smaller users to achieve optimal working height.

Standing workstations should be used for jobs that require a lot of body movement and greater force.

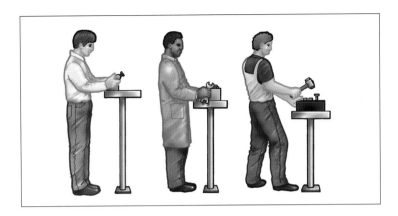

Figure 13

The most suitable working height depends upon the nature of the task being performed (See Figure 13)

Manipulative tasks (involving a moderate degree of both force and precision): table height should be 50-100 mm below elbow height.

Precision tasks (including writing): table height should be from 50-100 mm above elbow height.

Heavier tasks (particularly if they involve downward pressure to be applied on the work piece): table height should be from 00-250mm below elbow height.

The dimensions above are merely general guidelines and can be applied to both seated and standing work tasks. Given that individuals differ significantly in their build, elbow height, as a reference point will vary considerably from person to person. In addition, different types of tasks may require significantly different working height. It is therefore recommended that adjustable height surfaces be provided wherever possible. (It is not always the work surface height that has to be altered; platforms can be used to alter the effective height).

Sit/stand workstations enable workers to vary their working posture. For sit/stand workstations provide appropriate and adjustable chairs, adjustable tables or standing platforms. (See Figure 14).

Figure 14

Arm support	Provide support to the arms when they are raised if possible, and when precision work is being performed. Provide purpose built supports where needed to improve comfort and working posture.
Vision and lighting	Consider providing vision aids, if applicable, such as magnifying glasses. Ensure that lighting is suitable and adequate for the work undertaken.

Reducing force

General	Reduce forces required, especially when applied in combination with poor postures, eg use weaker springs in triggers, and use other power sources rather than muscle power. Reduce frequency with which force needs to be applied (see also 'Reducing repetition'). Reduce time spent applying force. This especially relates to static forces being applied and sustained for steadying or supporting items or gripping tools. Exerting excessive force often results from inappropriate working height for the task. For appropriate working heights refer to 'Optimising working postures'.
Work organisation and job design	Consider why high forces are necessary. Is it because of ill-fitting components, lack of maintenance or heavy items? Can this be addressed 'upstream' of this job? Through better maintenance? By reducing the weight of items, even those that are not lifted, but simply moved or accelerated manually.
Presentation/ orientation of work items	Consider altering the position or orientation of work pieces or tools so that any force can be applied more easily and efficiently ie improve the posture of the workers when applying forces (See 'Awkward posture').
Distribute force and enable stronger muscle groups to be used	Can foot pedals be used to provide force? Distribute force requirements over several fingers rather than one. Allow operators to use alternate hands to operate controls.

Mechanical advantage	Provide some means of increasing mechanical advantage, such as longer levers, or other means of mechanical assistance.
Gloves	Select appropriate gloves. Poor glove design or inappropriate choice of gloves or glove sizing can lead to poor sense of touch and increased effort in gripping.
Tools	Use light weight tools or provide supports, jigs or counterbalance devices. Hand tools should not require excessive force or have handles that are too large or small. They should not exert pressure or dig into the hand. (For more information see 'Tools'). Keep cutting edges sharp and moving parts appropriately lubricated.
Contact force or localised pressure	If there are sharp or hard contact points between equipment and workers consider removing, flattening or levelling.

Reducing duration

Generally	Allow for short breaks in work. Develop a work/rest regime which provides sufficient time for recovery. Monitor and manage overtime working. Consider job enlargement, job rotation.
Job rotation	Job rotation has the potential to reduce duration of exposure. Remember that rotating to a task that utilises the same parts of the body, and presents the same risk factors for injury, as the original task will not provide rest periods for parts of the body that are at risk of ULDs. When job rotation is introduced be aware of the following:

    □   training may be required to give the workers the necessary skills;

    □   skills used on one task may interfere with those on subsequent tasks and therefore, time for readjustment between tasks may be necessary;

> ☐   time may be needed to allow workers to get used to each job in the rotation sequence;
>
> ☐   rotation may have only a superficial impact upon risk exposure. In practice, the same level of physical demand may remain even though it appears to be quite different.

Environment

Vibration

Use low vibration equipment.

Ensure that tools are well maintained so as to reduce excess vibration.

Purchase tools with vibration damping or add vibration damping to existing tools.[45]

Minimise the amount of time that workers are using vibrating tools.

Anti-vibration gloves can be appropriate in some situations, however their impact on grip strength and type must be considered.

Ensure workers are trained in the risks associated with vibration.

Vision and lighting

Ensure task illumination is at a level that allows the worker to comfortably view the work piece without squinting or altering their posture.

Shadows or reflections, flickering lights and glare should also be controlled as they often cause people to adopt awkward postures.

All light sources should be regularly maintained.

Temperature and ventilation

Thermal conditions in the workplace should be such that all workers are reasonably comfortable regardless of seasonal variance.

Avoid positioning workstations in the vicinity of air vents as draughts may cause musculoskeletal discomfort.

Where possible ensure that tools and products handled by workers are not unduly cold.

Psychosocial

Job content

Reduce monotonous aspects, rotate workers between tasks.
Ensure reasonable workloads – assess speed of production.
Involve employees in determining workload.
Ensure a good climate of communication.
Ensure task clarity – clear performance requirements, feedback on performance and lines of reporting.
Encourage teamwork.
Monitor and manage overtime working. Overtime increases duration of exposure and decreases the time for recovery. There should be a break before starting overtime.

Work pressures

Ensure pay does not relate directly to production. Bonus systems and job-and-finish can increase the risks because they encourage people to work beyond their natural capacity. If there is a bonus system, try to reduce the extent of productivity relatedness, aim for a balance between bonus systems and workload.
Ensure a good climate of communication.
Develop an appropriate work rest schedule.
Allow for short breaks or micro pauses in work schedules.
Allow a gradual build up to full production speed, for example, when new workers start and when people return from absence.
Allow time for maintenance of tools, sharpening etc.

Tools

Selection

In selecting tools, a trial period with several workers is recommended. The purchaser should also have some knowledge of the task for which the tool will be used prior to selection.
It should be possible to use the tool in either hand – or provide a specific tool for left handed workers.

Size

Consider differences in male and female hand sizes, and the effect of wearing gloves.
Tools like pliers should not require a wide hand span, around 60 mm is good.

Handle design

Tool handles should enable a straight wrist posture (handshake) and avoid awkward hand and wrist postures. Ensure handles are long enough to fit the whole hand in a power grip.

Avoid rigid hard surfaced handles, sharp edges or narrow handles that place localised pressure on the hand.

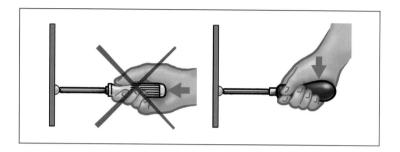

Figure 15

Force

Where not used as a safety device (ie 'dead man's handle') triggers and switches should not require continuous application of force. Provide trigger locks where operation is sustained (for more than about 30 seconds).

The operating force should be as low as possible. Triggers should enable operation by more than one finger. Return springs in cutting tools and pliers can help, but ensure the spring resistance is not too great.

Weight

Should be minimised, especially for precision work. Aim for around 1.5 kg and no more than 2.3 kg for power tools. Suspend the tool or use counterbalances.

Figure 16

Vibration

Purchase low vibration equipment.

Ensure that tools are well maintained. Ask tool suppliers for vibration data related to how you will use the tool and for advice on safe use, eg daily maximum useage time. Keep tools well maintained to retain lowest vibration performance and keep sharp. Blunt tools are less effective and mean longer exposure time for the operator.[45]

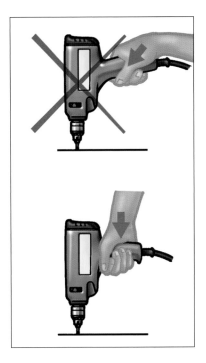

Figure 17 Illustrates vibration and optimal wrist posture

Appendix 3: **Medical aspects of upper limb disorders (ULDs)**

1   This section provides outline details for a range of disorders that medical practitioners commonly diagnose. It is not intended to be a definitive medical reference for such disorders or a method of self-diagnosis. It also gives guidance on the health management of ULDs, covering issues such as treatment and rehabilitation and occupational health support. Health management is an important aspect of the overall management of ULDs in your workplace.

Introduction

2   ULDs are conditions which affect the muscles, tendons, ligaments, nerves or other soft tissues and joints. The upper limb includes the neck, shoulders, arms, wrists, hands and fingers. The limb can be thought of as a mechanical system made up of rigid links, (the bones), moving at joints, which are held together by ligaments and surrounding tissues (capsules). Muscles are attached to these bones by tendons, which transmit the force produced during muscle contraction across a joint, resulting in movement of the bone and the limb segment, to which the muscle is attached.

3   Muscular activity can be either static or dynamic. Static effort is used to support or position the limb and hold it in space. Dynamic effort results in movement. For example, when cutting a piece of wood one arm is moved to cut the wood and hold the saw, while the other works statically in holding and steadying the wood. Movements depend on a complex pattern of muscle activation. The energy needed for muscle action comes through the blood supply, which also removes waste metabolic products. Tendons are smooth and slippery and in places are covered by synovial tissue. This produces a fluid to lubricate movement and is particularly found in many of the tendons of the wrist and hand.

4   Various theories exist to explain how upper limb disorders arise within the tissues and one recognised model details the interaction of exposure, dose, response and capacity.[17]

5   The pathophysiological processes involved may include disruption and deformation of tissue structures as a result of physical loading or compression, changes in the metabolism of muscle and other tissues, or the effect of factors such as infection, inflammation, degeneration and the immune response. Personal factors such as age, sex, pregnancy, genetics, body shape, medical history, nutritional status, personality and behaviour also have an influence on presentation, progress and recovery.

ULD complaints

6   Symptoms and signs associated with ULDs include the following:

- pain;
- ache or discomfort;
- tenderness;
- swelling.

7   Abnormal sensations that may occur are:

- numbness;
- tingling;
- pins and needles;
- burning sensation;
- feeling of warmth;
- cramp.

8   Other observations may include:

- stiffness;
- impairment of movement;
- weakness;
- reduced grip;
- muscle spasms.

9   Signs of ULDs can be minimal or absent at examination but this may depend on the experience of the health professional in examining the musculoskeletal system. Guidance is available to assist doctors in the assessment of symptoms and signs.[35]

10   Signs that can be detected might include:

- an appearance of swelling or deformity;
- changes in skin colour;
- tenderness on touching the affected part;
- a sensation of 'crackling' (called crepitus) when tendons are moved;
- touching particular area of skin may precipitate symptoms. If these are elicited the areas may be referred to as trigger points;
- joint movement may be restricted and painful;
- loss of muscle power may be seen in functions such as grasping and gripping;
- the response to stimulating the skin may be reduced or lost (loss of sensation to touch).

11   Upper limb disorders fall into one of two broad categories, those conditions that are recognised as discrete diseases with characteristic features, and non-specific pain syndromes where it is not possible to define a specific underlying cause for the pain, which is the principal characteristic feature of the disorder.

Recognised medical diseases

12   These can be grouped by the main anatomical structures involved as the following examples show:

- tendon-related disorders: tenosynovitis, DeQuervain's disease of wrist, tendinitis, trigger finger, epicondylitis;
- nerve-related disorders: Peripheral nerve entrapment (median, radial, ulnar nerves);
- muscle-related disorders: writer's cramp;
- neurovascular disorders: The sensorineural and vascular components of the hand-arm vibration syndrome;
- joint related disorders: osteoarthritis, shoulder capsulitis, ganglion;
- soft tissue disorders: beat hand, beat elbow, Dupuytren's contracture.

13   These conditions are usually diagnosed by the nature of onset and progression over time, of certain symptoms and the presence of clinical signs on examination. The essential defining features of a range of common ULDs have been detailed and the criteria for identification agreed at a consensus medical conference.[46]

14   In the process of a clinical assessment, some special tests may be required to check for general medical conditions or to confirm the diagnosis, eg blood tests for evidence of rheumatic disease or endocrine disturbance, or a urine test for diabetes. Occasionally specialist confirmatory tests are required, eg electrical tests of nerve conduction or muscle function, or imaging tests such as X-rays, bone scan, or Magnetic Resonance Imaging (MRI).

Non-specific pain syndromes

15   In many individuals a specific disease might not be identifiable and then the appropriate descriptor to use is the main symptom complaint ie pain and its anatomical location. Non-specific arm pain can be compared with non-specific low back pain (LBP), where it is also not possible to precisely define a specific underlying cause for the pain. Such non-specific pain syndromes are no less real than the discrete conditions and the impact on function may be equally severe. Medical enquiry should consider such features as:

- site and time of onset of pain;
- character, intensity, frequency, duration and radiation of pain;
- precipitating factors;
- provoking, relieving factors;
- influence of rest and activity (work, home, leisure);
- associated symptoms;
- psychosocial factors.

16   Most of us will experience arm pain at some time and for the majority it will be a brief self-limiting episode and not indicative of serious harm. However in situations where pain does not improve with rest, if it is disturbing sleep, recurring or persisting in nature then medical advice should be sought.

17   In a minority it can be said that pain itself becomes the disease rather than being solely a symptom of disease. This is thought to arise because the stimulus of pain has the potential to make the nervous system more responsive to further stimulation, a process known as neural sensitisation. This mechanism underlies the development of prolonged and progressive symptoms in some people, where arm pain becomes severe and chronic, with impaired use of the limb and the development of a permanent disability. This may be difficult to treat and is likely to require a trial of a combination of interventions including behavioural therapy. The rationale of early assessment, advice, appropriate treatment where indicated, and adjustments to work, should assist in preventing, or at least reducing the impact of such cases and reduce the burden of ill health.

An A-Z of upper limb disorders

Disorder	Description	Association with occupational activity*
BURSITIS/CELLULITIS (beat elbow, beat hand)	A distension of the fluid sac (bursa) and/or infection of the subcutaneous tissues. The bursa and the overlying skin may also become infected. Beat hand is an infection in the palm of the hand. Redness, heat, swelling and pain at relevant anatomical site.	Associated with repeated local trauma from prolonged leaning, or pressure, friction over elbow. Use of hand tools eg hammers and shovels, together with abrasion from dirt/dust.
CARPAL TUNNEL SYNDROME	A peripheral nerve disorder resulting from compression of the median nerve as it enters the palm of the hand. Tingling, numbness, tenderness can occur several hours after activity and appear in the parts of the hand innervated by the median nerve, (mainly in the thumb, index, middle and side of ring finger).	Associated with; - highly repetitive work; - forceful work; - hand arm vibration. Strong association with a combination of risk factors eg force, repetition and posture.

*These associations are derived from the NIOSH review of the epidemiological literature or relevant authors.[7]

	Characteristic intensification at night and relief gained by hanging the arm over the side of bed. Weakness of gripping and clumsiness.	
CRAMP OF THE HAND	A focal dystonia, which affects the control and co-ordination of muscle activity. Spasm of the muscles in the hand or forearm is observed. This often occurs when initiating specific movements and the effect may impair the use of the entire limb. It generally prevents the intended action from being performed. During an episode there may be stiffness or tightness in the hand.	Associated with prolonged periods of repetitive movements of the fingers, hand or arm.
CUBITAL TUNNEL SYNDROME	A peripheral nerve disorder resulting from compression of the ulnar nerve at the elbow. It causes medial elbow pain and tenderness and numbness and tingling in the ring and little finger. There may be weakness of movement of these fingers, impaired grip and clumsiness.	Associated with direct pressure or trauma.
DE QUERVAIN'S DISEASE	A localised swelling involving two tendons that move the thumb and which pass through a fibrous tunnel in the wrist. Activity related discomfort is experienced over the radial aspect of the wrist and forearm. Use of the hand and thumb for grasping becomes increasingly painful.	Associated with; - repetition; - force; - posture. Strong association with a combination of these risk factors. Can be associated with direct trauma of the radial aspects of the wrist.

DUPUYTREN'S CONTRACTURE	A thickening of the tissue below the skin in the palm of the hand which results in a progressive contracture appearing, especially of the ring and little finger of one or both hands. It is a painless thickening, possibly with a palpable nodule in the palmar crease. One or more fingers can curl up and cannot be straightened.	No generally accepted associations
EPICONDYLITIS (Tennis/Golfer's elbow)	A degeneration or inflammation of the short tendonous attachments from the forearm muscles to the bone at the elbow. On the inside of the arm these attach at the medial epicondyle and on the outside at the lateral epicondyle. Local tenderness is felt at the attachment of the tendon and is commonly known as tennis elbow (lateral epicondylitis) or golfers elbow (medial epicondylitis). Pain can radiate into the forearm and is activity dependant. There may be weakness of grip.	Associations with forceful work activities. Strong association with combinations of risk factors; force, repetition, posture.
GANGLION	A cyst filled with synovial fluid arising from a joint or tendon sheath and usually found on the back of the hand or wrist. The swelling can vary in size and be tense and firm or soft and squeezable and is usually painless.	No generally accepted associations
OSTEOARTHRITIS	A disturbance in the smooth articular cartilage surfaces which line joints, with associated changes in the	Occupational exposures may modify this disease process.

	surrounding bone, including bony overgrowth. This can affect any articulating joint, which in the upper limb includes those in the neck, shoulder, elbow, wrist, thumb and fingers. Symptoms include stiffness and aching pain on movement of the affected joint. Pain may radiate from neck into the arm (known as referred pain). There may be limitation in the full range of joint movement and bony swellings. Sometimes there is a grating noise on movement (crepitus).	
ROTATOR CUFF TENDINITIS – BICIPITAL TENDINITIS	An inflammation or degeneration of the tendons in the region of the shoulder joint. Symptoms are aching and pain in the shoulder which may be provoked by lying on the affected side at night. There is limitation of certain shoulder movements dependent on what tendon is affected. In bicipital tendonitis pain is experienced in the front of the shoulder and on raising the arm in front.	Associated with highly repetitive work and shoulder postures greater than 60 degrees flexion, abduction.
SHOULDER CAPSULITIS (Frozen shoulder)	An inflammation or degeneration of shoulder joint tissue. There is a gradual onset of stiffness and pain in the shoulder which is more severe at night and with increasing restriction in all shoulder movements.	No generally accepted associations

STENOSING TENOSYNOVITIS (Trigger finger/thumb)	A tendon sheath swelling in one of the tendons that cross the palm of the hand and run down the palmar surface of the finger/thumb. This restricts tendon movement through a fibrous ring termed a pulley. Triggering, clicking or catching felt on straightening the fingers or thumb and is often worse in the morning. A tender nodule is felt in the palm just beyond the base of the finger.	Possible association with overuse.
TENOSYNOVITIS	An inflammation of tendon sheaths at the wrist. Aching and pain is felt in the affected tendon which is worse on movement. Usually there is local tenderness and swelling. The overlying skin may appear red and warm with a grating feeling felt over the tendon (crepitus) during movement. Grasping and pinching may be weak depending upon the tendon affected.	Associated with; - repetition; - force; - posture. Strong association with a combination of these risk factors
VIBRATION WHITE FINGER	This is a disorder arising from impairment of blood circulation in the fingers and occurs in periodic attacks usually provoked by cold. The finger/s turn white (blanch) with associated numbness and tingling. Restoration of blood flow results in painful red throbbing fingers. In severe cases there is blanching of most fingers, co-ordination and dexterity is impaired.	Associated with exposure to vibration transmitted to the hand and arm from work processes

Treatments and rehabilitation

18   Acute ULDs are generally curable if recognised early and accurately diagnosed. Even where symptoms have become chronic and severe, occupational rehabilitation can be successful. The approach to most pain from acute ULDs is to rest the limb and reduce soft-tissue inflammation. Additional actions may be concerned with increasing muscle strength, range of joint movement and functional capacity.

19   One of the most effective means of resting the affected part is to reduce or eliminate exposure to the tasks which may have contributed to the onset of the condition, whether these arise in occupational or non-occupational activity, or in both settings. A short period of complete rest may be helpful particularly if inflammation is present. Protracted rest should be avoided unless under medical supervision as this can lead to deconditioning and weakening of the muscles and associated structures.

20   Anti-inflammatory drugs and analgesic medications, 'pain killers,' can be taken during this time. In the short term, the use of painkillers may allow continuation of work. This runs the risk, however, of exacerbating or prolonging the episode of ill health if work activity is a contributory or aggravating factor to an individual's symptoms. Local areas of tendon inflammation can be treated with steroid and local anaesthetic injections during the period of rest. Their effectiveness is compromised if risk factors in work activities are not also reduced or eliminated.

21   Immobilisation by appropriate splinting or support of the symptomatic area can be used, but this needs to be carefully supervised as there is a risk of weakening the limb. The regular use of supportive bandaging in a workplace to assist individuals suffering arm pain should however be discouraged. This is unlikely to be effective treatment on its own, and it indicates that there is an underlying problem which should be tackled.

22   Physiotherapy and occupational therapy practitioners can provide a range of treatments to assist with the restoration of function and rehabilitation. This might include specific exercises and/or stretching of muscles and nerves, joint mobilisation, electrotherapy, ultrasound, cold and heat applications. Some experts consider that more specialised 'neurodynamic' techniques can be of benefit where pain is the main problem, although this approach remains controversial. Practitioners of manipulative therapies such as osteopaths and chiropractors can also provide treatments and advice on rehabilitation and prevention.

23   Specialist opinion should ideally be obtained from practitioners who have experience in the recognition, treatment and management of ULDs. This could include physicians specialising in rheumatology, musculoskeletal medicine, neurology, psychology, and pain control. Specialists in occupational medicine can advise on workplace issues. Specialist opinion might involve referral to specialists in hand, orthopaedic or plastic surgery or, neurosurgery.

24　Surgical options are usually considered after less invasive treatment approaches have been tried. How quickly after surgery an employee is able to return to work will depend on the success of the surgery and the post-operative recovery. The extent to which ergonomic hazards in the workplace have been modified, and the results of an occupational health assessment are also relevant to recovery.

25　Treatment for chronic non-specific arm pain usually requires a detailed approach to be taken to the individual sufferer. A number of interventions are likely to be needed to stop the progression of symptoms, give the individual a sense of control over their pain and avoid deterioration in mental health. Therapeutic measures are based on a reduction of stress, by attention to physical or psychological stresses, counselling and relaxation therapies and pain relief (tricyclic medication, trigger point therapy, electrical stimulation, injections around nerves and acupuncture are possible approaches).

26　Complementary treatments are offered by a variety of therapists and include acupuncture, homeopathy, and yoga, as examples. There is little research on which to base the selection, or assess the effectiveness, of such therapies for managing ULDs.

Occupational health provision

27　Occupational health broadly embraces the issues concerning prevention of illness from work, managing the effects of illness at work and promoting health. In the context of ULDs, occupational health services could assist with:

- identification of health hazards, assessment of risk, and advice on control methods;
- advice on work placement of employees and medical fitness for particular work duties;
- provision of appropriate on-site first aid and treatment facilities;
- identifying causes of ill health within the workforce and liaison with other health care professionals, taking account of medical confidentiality, and the need to obtain an individual's consent;
- advising on suitable health surveys, the analysis and interpretation of health data and undertaking health related interviews or examinations;
- developing protocols for the management of ULDs in the workplace including rehabilitation, exercise programmes and return to work arrangements;
- advice on adjustments to work, or working arrangements, to support and maintain employment.

Where to get help

28   There are various ways in which occupational health support might be arranged, including provision of an in-house service or use of external providers. The larger occupational health services will be led by a doctor or nurse and may be part of a multidisciplinary health and safety team. These may be private providers, public providers such as an NHS trust, co-operative groups, or 'group occupational health services'. Other services come from independent occupational health physicians and nurses or from general practitioners and practice nurses working in occupational health. Professional bodies can provide lists of practitioners (see Further information).

29   HSE's Employment Medical Advisory Service (EMAS) can advise on occupational health services available in your local area and can give general advice on the management of the health effects of ULDs in the workplace.

30   Where an individual has an ongoing disability, assistance with workplace assessment and adjustment can be accessed through the local Disability Service Team at the Department for Work and Pensions (DWP).

Appendix 4:   **Legal requirements**

General

1   Employers have legal responsibilities to ensure the health and safety at work of their employees, and this includes the prevention of accidents and work related ill health such as ULDs. The Health and Safety at Work etc Act 1974[19] places general duties on employers and others. There are also a number of Regulations which impose specific requirements, and those most relevant to the prevention of ULDs include:

■   Management of Health and Safety at Work Regulations;[20]
■   Workplace (Health, Safety and Welfare) Regulations;[47]
■   Health and Safety (Display Screen Equipment) Regulations;[5]
■   Provision and Use of Work Equipment Regulations;[48]
■   Personal Protective Equipment at Work Regulation;[49]
■   Manual Handling Operations Regulations;[50]
■   Reporting of Injuries, Diseases and Dangerous Occurances Regulations 1995 (RIDDOR).[38, 39, 40]

2   The following paragraphs summarise those parts of the law that are particularly relevant to prevention of ULDs. They provide pertinent information on the regulations and associated guidance and approved code of practice (where relevant), but does not attempt to give a comprehensive general summary of each piece of legislation.

Health and Safety at Work etc Act 1974[19]

3   The Act imposes duties on everyone concerned with work activities, including employers, self-employed, employees, manufacturers and designers. The duties are imposed both on individual people and on corporations, companies, partnerships, local authorities etc. The duties are expressed in general terms so that they apply to all types of work activity and situations.

4   Section 2 of the Act puts a duty on all employers to ensure, so far as is reasonably practicable, the health, safety and welfare at work of all their employees. The most important areas relate to:

■   the provision and maintenance of plant (eg machinery and equipment), and systems of work such that they are safe and without risks to health;
■   the use, handling, storage and transport of articles and substances at work;
■   the provision of information, instruction, training and supervision, as necessary;

- the provision and maintenance of a working environment that is safe and free of risks to health.

5   In addition, a duty is placed on employers, unless exempted by the Act, to prepare and revise, as appropriate, a written statement of their general policy with respect to the health and safety at work of employees, the arrangements for carrying out the policy, and to bring it to the attention of employees. This applies to undertakings with five or more employees. Such policy statements should, where appropriate include reference to arrangements in place for the prevention of ULDs.

6   Section 3 of the Act places duties on employers to prevent other people, who are not their employees, being exposed to risks to their health and safety.

7   Section 7 of the Act places duties on employees to take reasonable care for the health and safety of themselves and of other persons who may be affected by what they do, or fail to do, at work.

Management of Health and Safety at Work Regulations 1999[20]

8   These Regulations set out broad general duties which apply to almost all kinds of work. They place a number of requirements on employers to:

- assess the risk to the health and safety of their employees and to anyone else who may be affected by their activity, so that the necessary preventive and protective measures can be identified;
- the assessment should take into account risks relating to new or expectant mothers (this is relevant because pregnancy can affect ULD risks due to hormonal changes which affect ligaments, posture, blood pressure and cause fatigue);
- make arrangements for putting into practice the health and safety measures that follow from the risk assessment. This covers planning, organisation, control, monitoring and review, ie the management of health and safety;
- provide such health surveillance as is appropriate having regard to the health and safety risks which are identified by the assessment;
- appoint competent people to help devise and apply the measures needed to comply with employers' duties under health and safety law (see paragraphs 39-40);
- give employees information about health and safety matters;
- co-operate with any other employers who share a work site;
- provide information to people working in their undertaking who are not their employees;
- make sure that employees have adequate health and safety training and are capable enough at their jobs to avoid risk; and give some particular health and safety information to temporary workers, to meet their special needs.

9   The Regulations also:

■   place duties on employees to follow health and safety instructions and report
     danger;
■   require employers to consult employees' safety representatives and provide
     facilities for them. Consultation must take place on such matters as the
     introduction of measures that may substantially affect health and safety; the
     arrangements for appointing competent persons; health and safety information
     and training required by law; and health and safety aspects of new technology
     being introduced to the workplace.

Workplace (Health, Safety and Welfare) Regulations 1992[47]

10   The aim of the regulations is to ensure that workplaces meet the health, safety and
     welfare needs of each member of the workforce. As well as factories, shops and offices the
     regulations cover schools, hospitals, hotels, places of entertainment, roads and paths on
     industrial estates, and temporary work sites (but not construction sites as they are
     covered by separate legislation - Construction (Health, Safety and Welfare) Regulations
     1996[51] and The Construction (Design and Management) Regulations 1994.[52]

11   The Regulations expand on employer's duties in section 2 of the Health and Safety at
     Work etc. Act 1974, and are intended to protect the health and safety of everyone in the
     workplace, and to ensure that adequate welfare facilities are provided for those at work.

12   Various aspects of the workplace are covered including:

■   workstations and seating: workstations should be arranged so that each task
     can be carried out safely and comfortably in terms of height of the work surface
     and accessibility to necessary items, with freedom of movement
■   maintenance of the workplace, and of equipment, devices and systems.
     Equipment should be maintained in efficient working order
■   temperature in indoor workplaces: during working hours the temperature in
     workplaces inside buildings should provide reasonable comfort without need
     for special clothing (special circumstances apply, eg for food handling)
■   lighting: this should be sufficient to enable people to work and use facilities.
     Where necessary, local lighting should be provided at individual workstations.

Health and Safety (Display Screen Equipment Regulations) 1992[5]

13   The Regulations apply where workers habitually use display screen equipment, such as
     computers, as a significant part of their normal work. In terms of preventing ULDs they
     require employers to:

- assess and reduce risks: the main health problems include upper limb pains and discomfort; temporary visual fatigue (possibly leading to the adoption of awkward postures which can cause further discomfort in the upper limbs); fatigue due to poor workstation, tasks or environment design, and stress;

- ensure workstations meet minimum requirements. In most cases the display screen should swivel and tilt, be free of reflections and glare and have a clear, stable image. The keyboard should tilt and be separate from the screen, with legible keys. The workstation should be sufficiently large to allow flexibility and comfort. The work chair should be stable, comfortable, adjustable in height and the back should adjust in height and tilt. A footrest should be made available, if needed. The environment such as space, lighting, heat and humidity should be adequate, and software should be suitable and easy to use;

- plan breaks or changes of activity. Timing and duration of these are not stipulated in the Regulations as it depends on the nature of the work. However breaks should be included in the working time, preferably short frequent breaks away from the screen and taken before the onset of fatigue;

- provide health and safety information and training;

- provide eye tests on request, and special spectacles if required for DSE work.

Provision and Use of Work Equipment Regulations 1998[48]

14   The Regulations place general duties on employers and list minimum requirements for work equipment to deal with hazards in all types of industry. The Regulations require employers in all industries to ensure that work equipment is suitable for the purpose and safe to use. 'Work equipment' covers everything from a hand tool, through machines of all kinds, to a connected series of machines such as a production line. The term 'use' includes starting, stopping, programming, setting, transporting, repairing, modifying, maintaining, servicing and cleaning. The Regulations require that work equipment is suitable and safe for the work carried out and does not pose any health or safety risk.

15   The general duties require employers to:

- take into account the working conditions and risks in the workplace when selecting equipment;

- make sure that equipment is suitable for the intended use and that it is used with suitable safety measures;

- ensure that it is properly maintained and inspected as necessary;

- take account of ergonomic risks when selecting work equipment, (ie ensure that equipment and operating positions, working heights, reach distances etc. are compatible with the intended operator);

- give adequate information, instruction and training on use of the equipment before use.

Personal Protective Equipment at Work Regulations 1992[49]

16   The Regulations place a duty on employers to ensure that suitable personal protective equipment (PPE) is provided to employees who may be exposed to a risk to their health and safety while at work, in circumstances where such risks cannot be adequately controlled by other means. PPE should take into account ergonomic requirements of the person who wears it and be capable of fitting the wearer correctly.

17   An example of PPE is hand and arm protection which is used to provide protection against a range of industrial hazards, but which may also reduce the ability to grip and contribute to ULDs.

Manual Handling Operations Regulations 1992[50]

18   These regulations apply to all manual handling tasks, ie tasks which involve transporting, such as lifting, pushing, pulling or supporting a load. In work places, there are a wide range of handling and transporting processes taking place, ranging from assembly line work, lifting boxes, bags and components, to helping people with limited mobility with their day to day activities. The Regulations apply to operations which can cause injury not only to the back but may also affect all parts of the body including the upper limbs.

19   The regulations place duties on the employer to:

■   avoid the need for undertaking any manual handling operations at work which involve a risk of being injured, so far as is reasonably practicable;
■   where it is not reasonably practicable to avoid risk of injury, carry out an assessment of the risks to take into account the task, load, working environment and the worker's individual capability to carry out the task. HSE guidance on the regulations provides guidelines for lifting loads; the maximum weight depends on factors such as height of the lift, the distance that the object is extended from the body, whether the employee is male or female, and whether sitting or standing;
■   where it is not reasonably practicable to avoid risk of injury, to take appropriate steps to reduce the risk of injury from hazardous manual handling to the lowest level reasonably practicable.

Reporting of Injuries, Diseases and Dangerous Occurrences Regulations 1995 (RIDDOR)[38]

20   RIDDOR places a duty on employers, on the self-employed and on those in control of

work premises to report certain work-related accidents, diseases, and dangerous occurrences to the enforcing authorities (HSE or local authorities). If a doctor diagnoses and reports to an employer that an employee is suffering from a reportable work-related disease, and the person concerned is currently employed in an associated work activity, then the employer must send, either by post or electronically via the HSE website, a completed disease report form to the relevant enforcing authority.

21   In terms of ULDs, the diseases which in specified circumstances are reportable are cramp of the hand or forearm, subcutaneous cellulitis of the hand, bursitis or subcutaneous cellulitis arising at or about the elbow, traumatic inflammation of the tendons of the hand or forearm, carpal tunnel syndrome and hand-arm vibration syndrome (although the latter is outside the scope of this guidance).

References

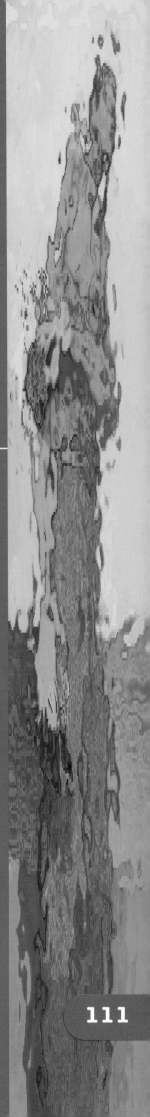

References Cited in Text

1 *Securing health together: A long term occupational health strategy for England, Scotland and Wales* Misc 225 HSE Books 2000

2 *Revitalising Health and Safety: Strategy Statement June 2000 The Stationery Office 2000.* Further copies are available from Department of the Environment, Transport and the Regions, Free Literature Service, PO Box 236, Wetherby, West Yorkshire LS23 7NB. Tel: 0870 1226 236 Fax: 0870 1226 237 Website: http://www.detr.gov.uk/pubs/index.htm

3 *Hand-arm vibration* HSG88 HSE Books 1994 ISBN 0 7176 0743 7

4 *Mechanical Vibration: Guidelines for the measurement and assessment of human exposure to hand-transmitted vibration. Part 2: Practical guidance for measurement at the workplace* First Edition ISO 5349-2 2001

5 *Display screen equipment work. Health and Safety (Display Screen Equipment) Regulations 1992. Guidance on Regulations* L26 HSE Books 1992 ISBN 0 7176 0410 1

6 *Working with VDU's* Leaflet INDG36(rev1) HSE Books 1998 (single copy free or priced packs of 10 ISBN 0 7176 1504 9)

7 Bernard B P and Putz-Anderson V (editors) *Musculoskeletal disorders and workplace factors. A critical review of epidemiological evidence for work-related musculoskeletal disorders of the neck, upper extremity and lower back* National Institute for Occupational Safety and Health DHHS (NIOSH) Publication No.97-1411997

8 Hunter D *The Diseases of Occupations* (Ninth edition) Arnold London 2000 ISBN 0 34067750 3

9 Cherry N et al 'Surveillance of work-related diseases by occupational physicians in the UK: OPRA 1996-1999' *Occupational Medicine* 2000 **50** (7) 496-503.

10 Cherry N et al 'The reported incidence of work-related musculoskeletal disease in the UK: MOSS 1997-2000' *Occupational Medicine* 2001 **51** (7) 450-455

11 Mackay C et al *Musculoskeletal disorders in supermarket cashiers* HSE Books 1998 ISBN 0 7176 0831 X

12 *Work-Related Upper Limb Disorders: A Review of the Evidence* National Research Council Washington DC National Academy Press 1998 ISBN 0 30906327 2

13 Jones J R and Hodgson J T *Self reported work related Illness in 1995: Results from a household survey* HSE Books 1998 ISBN 0 7176 1509 X and Jones JR, Hodgson JT and Osman J *Self reported working conditions in 1995* HSE Books 1997 ISBN 0 7176 1449 2

14 *Information sheet 2/99/EMSU Economic Impact: Revised data from Self-reported Work-related Illness survey in 1995 (SWI95)* Available from HSE's Epidemiology and Medical Statistics Unit and HSE's website www.hse.gov.uk

15 Chaffin D and Andersson G (editors) *Occupational biomechanics* (Third edition) Wiley 1999 ISBN 0 4712 4697 2

16 Whiting W and Zernicke R (editors) *Biomechanics of musculoskeletal injury* Leeds Human Kinetics 1998 ISBN 0 87322779 4

17   Armstong T, Buckle P, Fine L et al. 'A conceptual model for work-related neck and upper-limb musculoskeletal disorders. *Scandinavian Journal of Work Environment & Health* 1993 1973-84

18   Buckle P and Devereux J *Work related neck and upper limb musculoskeletal disorders* European Agency for Safety and Health at Work Luxembourg 1999 ISBN 92 828 8174 1

19   *Health & Safety at Work etc Act 1974* Ch 3 The Stationery Office 1974 ISBN 0 10 543774 3

20   *Management of health and safety at work. Management of Health and Safety at Work Regulations 1999. Approved Code of Practice and guidance* L21 (Second edition) HSE Books 2000 ISBN 0 7176 2488 9

21   *Work related upper limb disorders; the development of an interactive database* HSE Contract research report. (To be published). For further information see 'other websites'.

22   *A guide to the Health and Safety (Consultation with Employees) Regulations 1996. Guidance on Regulations* L95 HSE Books 1996 ISBN 0 7176 1234 1

23   *Safety representatives and safety committees* L87 (Third edition) HSE Books 1996 ISBN 0 7176 1220 1

24   *A guide to the Offshore Installations (Safety Representatives and Safety Committees) Regulations 1989. Guidance on Regulations* L110 (Second edition) HSE Books 1998 ISBN 0 7176 1549 9

25   Haines HM and Wilson JR *Development of a framework for participatory ergonomics* CCR174 HSE Books 1998 ISBN 0 7176 1573 1

26   *Handle with care. Assessing musculoskeletal risks in the chemical industry* HSE Books 2000 ISBN 0 7176 1770 X

27   Li G and Buckle P *Evaluating change in exposure to risk for musculoskeletal disorders: A practical tool* CRR251 HSE Books 1999 ISBN 0 7176 1722 X

28   McAtamney L et al *Reducing the risks of work related upper limb disorders* Institute of Occupational Ergonomics Nottingham University 1992.

29   Buckle P *TUC Guide to assessing WRULD risks* Trade Union Congress, College Hill Press London 1994 ISBN 1 85006277 3

30   Li G and Buckle P (editors) 'Current techniques for assessing physical exposure to work-related musculoskeletal risks, with emphasis on posture based methods' *Ergonomics* 1999 **42** (5) 674-695

31   *Lighting at work* HSG38 (Second edition) HSE Books 1997 ISBN 0 7176 1232 5

32   *New and expectant mothers at work: A guide for employers* HSG122 HSE Books 1994 ISBN 0 7176 0826 3

33   *A pain in your workplace? Ergonomic problems and solutions* HSG121 HSE Books 1994 ISBN 0 7176 0668 6

34   Woods V and Buckle P *Research into practice – the value of case studies in reducing musculoskeletal problems in the cleaning industry. Proceedings Premus 2001,* Fourth International Scientific Conference on Prevention of Work-Related Musculoskeletal Disorders

35   Graves RJ, Sinclair DT et al *Development and evaluation of diagnostic support aids for upper limb disorders* CRR280 HSE Books 2000 ISBN 0 7176 1824 2

36   *Access to Medical Reports Act 1988 (c.28)* The Stationary Office ISBN 0 10 542888 4.

37   Cox R A et al *Fitness for Work: The Medical Aspects* (Third edition) Oxford University Press 2000 ISBN 0 19263043 1

38   *A guide to the Reporting of Injuries, Diseases and Dangerous Occurrences Regulations 1995* L73 (Second edition) HSE Books 1999 ISBN 0 7176 2431 5

39   *RIDDOR Reporting: Information about the new incident centre* MISC310 HSE Books 2001

40   *RIDDOR Explained* HSE 31(rev1) HSE Books 2001

41   *Social Security (Industrial Injuries)(Prescribed Diseases) Regulations 1985* The Stationery Office ISBN 0 11 056467 9

42   *Health surveillance at work* HSG61 (Second edition) HSE Books 1999 ISBN 0 7176 1705 X

43   *Health and safety benchmarking – Improving together: Guidance for those interested in applying benchmarking to health and safety* Leaflet INDG301 HSE Books 1999 (single copy free or priced packs of 10 ISBN 0 7176 2494 3)

44   *Seating at work* HSG57 (Second edition) HSE Books 1997 ISBN 0 7176 1231 7

45   *Vibration solutions: Practical ways to reduce the risk of hand-arm vibration injury* HSG170 HSE Books 1997 ISBN 0 7176 0954 5

46   Harrington JM et al 'Surveillance case definitions for work related upper limb pain syndromes' *Occupational and Environmental Medicine* 1998 **55** (4) 264 – 271

47   *Workplace health, safety and welfare. Workplace (Health, Safety and Welfare) Regulations 1992. Approved Code of Practice* L24 HSE Books 1992 ISBN 0 7176 0413 6

48   *Safe use of work equipment. Provision and use of work equipment regulations 1998. Approved code of practice and guidance* (Second edition) HSE Books 2001 ISBN 0 7176 1626 6

49   *Personal protective equipment at work. Personal Protective Equipment at Work Regulations 1992. Guidance on Regulations* L25 HSE Books 1992 ISBN 0 7176 0415 2

50   *Manual handling. Manual Handling Operations Regulations 1992. Guidance on Regulations* L23 (Second edition) HSE Books 1998 ISBN 0 7176 2415 3

51   *A guide to the Construction (Health, Safety and Welfare) Regulations* 1996 Leaflet INDG220 HSE Books 1996 (single copy free or priced packs of 10 ISBN 0 7176 1161 2)

52   *Managing construction for health and safety. Construction (design and management) regulations 1994. Approved code of practice* HSE Books 1995 ISBN 0 7176 0792 5

Further information

HSE publications

Jackson P R and Parker S K (editors) *Change in manufacturing: How to manage stress-related risks* HSE Books 2001 ISBN 0 7176 2086 7

Enforcement policy statement MISC030 HSE Books 2001

Sinclair DT, Graves RJ et al *Feasibility of developing a prototype decision aid for initial medical assessment of work-related upper limb disorders* CRR279 HSE Books 2000 ISBN 0 7176 1823 4

General ventilation in the workplace: Guidance for employers HSG202 HSE Books 2000 ISBN 0 7176 1793 9

Health risks from hand-arm vibration: Advice for employers Leaflet INDG175(rev1) HSE Books 1998 (single copy free or priced packs of 10 ISBN 0 7176 1553 7)

Cox T, Griffiths A, Barlow C et al *Organisational interventions for work stress: A risk management approach* HSE Books 2000 ISBN 0 7176 7838 2

Power tools: How to reduce vibration health risks - Guide for employers Leaflet INDG338 HSE Books 2001 (single copy free or priced packs of 15 ISBN 0 7176 2008 5)

Stating your business: Guidance on preparing a health and safety policy document for small firms Leaflet INDG324 HSE Books 2000 (single copy free or priced packs of 5 ISBN 0 7176 1799 8)

Successful health and safety management HSG65 (Second edition) HSE Books 1997 ISBN 0 7176 1276 7

McCaig R and Harrington M (editors) *The changing nature of occupational health* HSE Books 1998 ISBN 0 7176 1665 7

Thermal comfort in the workplace: Guidance for employers HSG194 HSE Books 1999 ISBN 0 7176 2468 4

Upper limb disorders: Assessing the risks Leaflet INDG171 HSE Books 1994 (single copy free or priced packs of 10 ISBN 0 7176 0751 8)

General Texts

Helander M *A Guide to the Ergonomics of Manufacturing* Taylor & Francis 1997
ISBN 0 7484 0122 9

Moon S D and Sauter S L (editors) *Beyond Biomechanics: Psychosocial aspects of musculoskeletal disorders at work* Taylor and Francis 1996 ISBN 0 7484 0321 3

Pheasant S *Bodyspace: Anthropometry, Ergonomics and the Design of Work* (Second edition) Taylor & Francis 1996 ISBN 0 7484 0067 2

Sluiter JK, Rest KM, Frings-Dresen MHW *Criteria document for the evaluation of the work-relatedness of upper extremity musculoskeletal disorders* Coronel Institute for Occupational and Environmental Health, University of Amsterdam, Netherlands 2000

Putz-Anderson V *Cumulative trauma disorders: A manual for musculoskeletal diseases of the upper limbs* Taylor & Francis 1998 ISBN 0 85066405 5

Dul J and Weerdmeester B (editors) *Ergonomics for beginners – A quick reference guide* (Third edition) Taylor & Francis 2000 ISBN 0 7484 0079 6

Pheasant S *Ergonomics, Work and Health* McMillan Press 1991 ISBN 0 30907284 0

O'Neil R *Europe Under Strain: A report on Trade Union initiative to combat workplace musculoskeletal disorders* TUTB Brussels 1999 ISBN 2 93000329 4

Wilson J R and Corlett E N (editors) *Evaluation of Human Work: A practical ergonomics methodology* Taylor & Francis 1995 ISBN 07484 0084 2

Kroemer K H E and Grandjean E (editors) *Fitting the Task to the Human* (Fifth edition) Taylor & Francis 1997 ISBN 0 7484 0665 4

Parker S K and Wall T D *Job and work design: organising work to promote well-being and effectiveness* Sage London 1998 ISBN 0 76190420 4

Musculoskeletal disorders and the workplace: Low back and upper extremities National Research Council National Academy Press 2001 ISBN 0 30907284 0

Kasdan M L 'Occupational hand injuries' *Occupational Medicine: State of the Art Reviews* 1989 **4** (3) 395-574

Hadler N M *Occupational Musculoskeletal Disorders* (Second edition) Lippincott Williams and Wilkins 1999 ISBN 0 78171495 8

Clark T S and Corlett E N (editors) *The ergonomics of workspaces and machines: A design manual* (Second edition) Taylor & Francis 1995 ISBN 0 7484 0320 5

Di Martino V and Corlett N (editors) *Work organisation and ergonomics* International Labour Office Geneva 1998 ISBN 9 22109518 5

Kuorinka I and Forcier L (editors) *Work related musculoskeletal disorders (WMSDs): A reference book for prevention* Taylor & Francis 1995 ISBN 0 7484 0131 8

Hutson M A *Work-related upper limb disorders: Recognition and management* Butterworth-Heinmann 1999 ISBN 0 75064548 2

Government bodies

Health and Safety Executive: www.hse.gov.uk

HSE Employment Medical Advisory Service – look for details of your local HSE office in the telephone directory or HSE web site.

Department of Health: www.doh.gov.uk

Department for Work & Pensions/Disability service team: www.disability.gov.uk

Local Authority Environmental Health Officers': contact the Environmental Health Office of your Local Authority

Professional and Other Associations

British Chiropractic Association
Blagrave House, 17 Blagrave Street
Reading, Berkshire. RG1 1QB
Tel: 0118 950 5950
Web: www.chiropractic-uk.co.uk

British Institute of Musculoskeletal Medicine
34 The Avenue
Watford, Herts. WD1 3NS
Tel: 01923 220999   Web: www.bimm.org.uk

Chartered Society of Physiotherapy
14 Bedford Row
London WC1R 4ED
Tel: 020 7306 6666
Scottish Office Tel: 0131 226 1441, Welsh Office Tel: 029 2038 2428
Web: www.csphysio.org.uk

College of Occupational Therapists
106-114 Borough High St
Southwark London SE1 1LB
Tel: 020 7357 6480
www.cot.co.uk

Faculty of Occupational Medicine of the Royal College of Physicians
6 St Andrew's Place
Regent's Park, London NW1 4LB
Tel: 020 7317 5890
Web: www.facoccmed.ac.uk

General Osteopathic Council
176 Tower Bridge Road
London SE1 3LU
Tel: 020 7537 6655
Web: www.osteopathy.org.uk

Institute of Occupational Safety and Health
The Grange, Highfield Drive
Wigston, Leicestershire LE18 1NN
Tel: 0116 257 3100
Web: www.iosh.co.uk

Occupational Therapy in Work Practice and Productivity
c/o Specialist Sections Officer
College of Occupational Therapists
106-17 Borough High Street
Southwark
London SE1 1LB
http://www.cot.co.uk/special/otwpp.htm.

Royal College of Nursing
20 Cavendish Square
London W1M 0AB.
Tel: 020 7409 3333
Web: www.rcn.org.uk

Society of Occupational Medicine
6 St Andrew's Place
Regent's Park, London , NW1 4LB
Tel: 020 7486 2641
Web: www.som.org.uk

The Association of Chartered Physiotherapists in
Occupational Health and Ergonomics (ACPOHE)
PO Box 121
London E17
Tel: 01964 534376
http://www.acpoh.co.uk

The Ergonomics Society
Devonshire House, Devonshire Square
Loughborough, Leicestershire LE11 3DW
Tel: 01509 234904
Web: www.ergonomics.org.uk

The RSI Association
380-384 Harrow Road
London W9 2HU
Tel: 020 7266 2000
Web: www.rsi-uk.org.uk

Other Websites

European Agency for Safety and Health at Work
Gran Via 33
E-48009 Bilbao Spain
Tel: +34 94 479 43 60
Email: information@osha.eu.int
Web: http://agency.osha.eu.int/ *and* http://europe.osha.eu.int/good_practice/risks/msd/

National Health Service
http://www.nhsplus.nhs.uk

National Institute for Occupational Health and Safety (NIOSH)(USA):
http://www.cdc.gov/niosh/homepage.html

Work related upper limb disorders: a database of court judgements
http://www.lboro.ac.uk/wruld-db

Printed and published by the Health and Safety Executive
HSG60(rev)   C200   2/02